PRO LIFE?

Dr Michael Solomons was born in Dublin in 1919. His father, Dr Bethel Solomons, was a leading gynaecologist and Master of the Rotunda. He was educated in Dublin, Switzerland and Scotland, qualified as a doctor at Dublin University in 1941, and then held postgraduate appointments in Irish and British hospitals. He served as a Medical Officer in the RAF and returned to Ireland in 1948, to specialize in gynaecology and obstetrics. He became a member of staff of several Dublin hospitals: Mercer's, Baggot Street and the Rotunda. He is a Fellow of the Royal College of Physicians in Ireland, and of the Royal College of Obstetricians and Gynaecologists. He is President of the Irish Association of Family Planning Doctors. He retired from practice in 1988, but is still involved with the Irish Family Planning Association. He lives in Dublin and is married with four children and two grandchildren.

PRO LIFE?

THE IRISH QUESTION

MICHAEL SOLOMONS

THE LILLIPUT PRESS

First published in 1992 by
THE LILLIPUT PRESS LTD
4 Rosemount Terrace, Arbour Hill,
Dublin 7, Ireland.

A CIP record for this
title is available from
The British Library.

ISBN 1 874675 02 3

Cover design by Jarlath Hayes
Set in 11 on 13 Stempel Garamond by
MERMAID TURBULENCE
Printed in Dublin by ßetaprint on recycled paper.

CONTENTS

ILLUSTRATIONS

(all photographs by courtesy of Derek Speirs /Report)

ACKNOWLEDGMENTS

Many of my friends and colleagues have generously helped with information, encouragement and advice, for which I am deeply grateful. I especially wish to mention the professional skills of Anthea McTeirnan, who reduced the original unwieldy manuscript to its present form.

INTRODUCTION

Anyone who recalls the bitterness of the 1983 abortion referendum is unlikely to welcome a repeat performance. I would like to introduce a different note by describing the history of some developments in Irish society which are relevant to the current issues.

The debate on the substantive issue of abortion is being held against a backdrop of a medical service for women in Ireland which has altered and improved almost beyond recognition since I began my career in 1939. Some basic statistics will demonstrate this. In the Rotunda Hospital, Dublin, between 1948 and 1951, when 12,010 deliveries took place, twenty-three women and 800 babies died. Of the 18,293 deliveries that occurred at the hospital between 1988 and 1991, there were 177 infant deaths and one maternal death.

Family size has decreased dramatically in the last half-century. Some 23 per cent of the women who were delivered in the Rotunda in 1943 had already been pregnant nine times. By 1990 only 10.5 per cent of women who gave birth were on their fifth or later pregnancy. Access to contraception, coupled with education and information about sex, have had a part to play in reducing family size and the incidence of maternal and infant deaths. Improvements in medical procedure, drugs and technology have also helped. Nowadays women are given information and prepared for labour. Antenatal care is not just better, it is more comprehensive, being available to all women who want it. Anaesthetics have improved and we have a better grasp of techniques for relieving pain. Abnormalities in the foetus and placenta can be picked up by using ultra-sound scanning and thus possible complications at birth can be catered for. Electronic foetal monitoring allows medical and nursing staff to recognize a baby who is in distress at an earlier stage. Caesarean section is safer and a life-saving alternative to the difficult, assisted vaginal deliveries of the past. Infant intensive care is now available, saving the lives of the sick and premature. Blood transfusion and antibiotics have greatly helped.

Not all of these life-enhancing changes were easily come by. The provision of contraception and information about contraception within Ireland was rigorously opposed by the Catholic Church and other conservative groups. As a founder member of the Irish Family Planning Association, and as a doctor who advocated family planning, I often found myself at the centre of controversy. While debates about contraception and other sex-related matters raged, the more conservative elements in Irish society threw their hands in the air and mourned the death of Catholic Ireland. From a position where there were no family planning clinics in the Republic until February 1969, there are now two in Limerick, one each in Cork, Tralee, Navan, Galway and Wexford, and seven in the Dublin area. These changes have not weakened the fabric of society, but have enhanced the quality of family life.

In 1983, believing that the proposed amendment to the Constitution outlawing abortion in Ireland would lead to confusion and affect standards of medical care and choice for Irish women, I joined the Anti-Amendment campaign. Only five years before my retirement I was again at the centre of a major controversy. During the course of that debate it became obvious that many people found the concept of abortion strange and frightening. Fear and ignorance can be exploited by those who have no integrity and no respect for the truth. I hoped then, and I hope now, that as an experienced practitioner in the world of women's medicine

I could give people the facts and contribute to their greater understanding of the issues. What follows is not an academic study, but a summary of my experiences and views after almost fifty years' work in this field.

'Women in a doorway', an etching by Estella F. Solomons (1882-1968)

ONE

1939 — 1951

In December 1939, as a medical student at the Rotunda Hospital, I first saw a baby born. It was to be the first of many. At the time pregnancy was dangerous for women the world over. However, Irish women were faced with a number of special factors that made the business of reproduction potentially even more dangerous. The social teaching of the Roman Catholic Church, to which the majority of Irish women subscribed, forbade the use of contraceptives. The moral stance of the Catholic Church built into the statute law of the fledgling Irish Republic via the Criminal Law Amendment Act of 1935, made it an offence to sell, offer, advertise, import or attempt to import any contraceptives. In years to come this law was to be copper-fastened by further legislative interventions.

The law had its human consequences. Ireland's birthrate was one of the highest in Europe. During a six-month period in 1943 when I was Clinical Clerk in the Rotunda, students attended 785 home deliveries. Ninety-three were to women pregnant for at least the tenth time. Of these, twenty-five were on their tenth pregnancy, twenty-three their eleventh, seventeen their twelfth, and fourteen were giving birth for the fourteenth time. One woman was admitted to the hospital miscarrying on her twenty-first pregnancy.

A woman who has given birth over seven times is referred to in medical jargon as a 'grand multipara'. The colourful term originated in Dublin. In 1933 *The Lancet* published a paper by my father, Bethel Solomons, a gynaecologist and then Master of the Rotunda, in which he set out the dangers of so many pregnancies for both mother and child. He called them not the grand multiparas but the 'dangerous multiparas'. In the thirties the medical problems associated with unrestricted pregnancy, such as high blood pressure and anaemia, were compounded by a paucity of antenatal care, a general lack of education and poor nutrition. Mothers and their babies suffered. Ultimately many died.

As an aspiring doctor I advised the women I saw to try and control the number of children they had. It was easier said than done. Many of the women pointed out to this naive young medic that abstinence from sex during an 'unsafe period' required a degree of self-control unknown to their husbands. Men had been taught to look upon sex as part of their marriage rights. In the 1930s the word contraception was missing from the national vocabulary. One English postgraduate, aware of the pressing need for contraception, returned from across the water with a supply of condoms. He had planned to give them to female patients when he visited them after their deliveries. However, he was dissuaded from doing so when his first 'customer' refused them saying, 'Thanks, doctor, but take them away, my husband would only throw them on the fire.'

Desperation bred ingenuity. As no mechanical means of contraception were available, people improvised. While attending one birth, a colleague came across the strange phenomenon of a baby born with the top of a Guinness bottle stuck on its head. The mother had hoped it would act as a contraceptive.

A high birthrate due to the absence of contraception, and a general lack of education about sex, meant that Irish maternity services came under a lot of pressure. In 1939 the gaps in such provision were obvious. For many years medical students in Dublin hospitals had delivered patients in their homes 'on the district'. In the case of the Rotunda, the district included most of north Dublin, including Whitehall, Cabra and the entire North Circular Road down to the Phoenix Park. The hospital was responsible for about two thousand home deliveries each year. At this time at least one-third of Dublin's babies were born either at home or in small nursing homes.

Students were unleashed on the public after they had received basic practical training in the labour ward. The 'training' was a confidence-sapping business. We wore thick rubber gloves. Continual boiling, soaking and storing in antiseptic solution meant that these cumbersome items became more of a hindrance than a help. Our clumsy deliveries would be supervised by a long-suffering ward sister who would issue a long stream of instructions: 'Keep your hands off, keep the head flexed, feel for the chin, let it come slowly, let it rotate, now put your hand around the neck – no, not that way, support its body with the other hand, don't drop it.' After attending ten deliveries we were sent out to 'help' the public. We would move around in packs of three. Newly trained students would be put into a group with an 'experienced' practitioner. 'Experienced' in those days meant that a student had spent a mere two weeks on the district.

In the nineteenth century the north side of Dublin had been a fashionable quarter. By the 1930s this had changed. The original four-storey buildings remained but their Georgian doors and fanlights had gone. Each building was now home to upwards of six families surviving in run-down flats where the paint peeled off the walls and the ceilings leaked. There was no electricity or running water, toilet facilities were primitive, and all the flats shared a communal tap located on the ground floor. The poorest families would often live in a single room. Dust, debris, poor facilities for waste disposal and the absence of a bath resulted in the prevalence of disease and infection. Tuberculosis and gastro-enteritis were common, the latter causing almost 1300 infant deaths in the County Dublin epidemic of 1941. Newer blocks of flats did exist, but with large numbers of children, high levels of unemployment and low incomes, it was impossible for most families to make their homes comfortable or to keep them in good repair.

Often the birth was the first time that a pregnant woman would come into contact with a member of the medical profession. Many gave birth to all their babies without ever seeing a doctor; some were delivered by their mothers, neighbours or friends; others preferred to see a midwife. While antenatal care did exist, lack of information and education for working-class women meant that many did not attend a hospital clinic. Avoidable complications were the result.

When a woman in labour wanted medical assistance a relation or neighbour would call to the hospital and ask for the district team. In the days before street directories, this person would then bring us to the patient. This stopped us getting lost. We would travel on foot, by bicycle or by bus. Sometimes we would arrive to find that the baby was already born. We had little expertise and even less equipment at our disposal. Our doctors' bags contained only a few basic implements: cord ties and scissors, antiseptic solution, a mucus extractor, a bladder catheter, rubber gloves, and a cheap cotton-wool substitute called tow. The most important piece of equipment by far was a torch. Wartime rationing meant that the gas supply, which was often the only source of heating and light, was turned off at the mains for a few hours each day. While it was possible to use the minimal supply remaining in the pipes, the family ran the risk of being caught by the 'glimmer man', an inspector who had the right to call at random and disconnect the gas if he found evidence that they had been breaking the law.

Female family and friends were often around and they gave us a warm welcome, calling us 'doctor' even though they were well aware that we were not qualified. We would arrive to find newspapers covering the mattress for protection and kettles and saucepans somehow full of boiling water ready for our instruments. We would often be working in a confined space. On one occasion we found ourselves in such a tight spot that a colleague had to shine the torch in from outside a caravan window so that we could see what we were doing. Often we would not be entirely sure that we were doing the right thing. Asking for guidance on how to give a woman an enema, my partner said simply, 'She'll tell you when to stop.' Although the environment in which many women found themselves giving birth was far from satisfactory and the medical help they received was patchy, Mother Nature took care of her charges pretty well. Provided that the baby seemed to be lying in the normal position, its heart sounded normal and its mother was reasonably at ease, each of us would take turns sitting on the bed, encouraging, reassuring and rubbing her back during contractions. Someone would be given the job of watching for the appearance of the baby's head and many an unsuspecting student received a splash in the face when a mother's waters broke. While in our amateurish way we would try to assess how a birth was progressing, the opinion of an experienced mother, or her friends, would often prove far more dependable than our own.

All of the students on the district were given a list of guide-lines. If a delivery was proving problematic for the mother or baby, one member of the team would return to the hospital and call out the Clinical Clerk, the CC. This doctor on the junior staff, who supervised the extern cases, would then assess the situation and decide if he could treat the patient safely in her own home or if she needed to be admitted into hospital. High blood pressure, foetal distress and delays in labour would often necessitate a trip into the Rotunda. During the few weeks that I spent on the district only a handful of patients required hospital treatment. One woman bled excessively after giving birth and we had to call out the CC to try and stop it. In those days without modern drugs and without the facilities for blood transfusion many women would bleed to death. A quarter of all calls we made on the district were to women who had spontaneously aborted. Callous though it might seem, we students were always disappointed to be called out to such cases as medical school regulations required that we each attend ten births, and abortions did not count.

Aware of the potential for complications, we felt a terrific sense of relief once a baby was born and crying. When a delivery was completed friends and neighbours would take over. A fresh nightdress and a cup of tea would be produced for the exhausted mother. The chamber-pot, often borrowed from a neighbour as not every family possessed one, would be gratefully returned and the bedclothes would be straightened. One doctor, the late Annesley de Courcy Wheeler, told me of the shock he received when he pulled back the blankets after a delivery to find another infant in the bed. Knowing that he had not delivered twins, he stared at his colleague in bemused silence until the mother explained, 'That was last year's, Doctor.'

I left my work on the district a wiser man. Bolstered by a deep religious faith, the courage and patience of these women seemed to know no bounds. Somehow they accepted our shortcomings and whatever their circumstances always provided us with tea and biscuits after a birth. The women could not have been unaware of the important part they played in our education and they never forgot a face. For years later I would be greeted by cries of 'How a' ya, Doctor?' from the fruit-sellers and fish-sellers as I strolled down Moore Street.

Qualifying in June 1941, I worked for a year in Baggot Street Hospital and three months in the National Children's Hospital before returning to the Rotunda to take a postgraduate course. There was no booking service for maternity patients at the Rotunda in those days and, as Irish hospitals never withheld their services from any woman in labour, many complicated cases appeared out of the blue. As the Rotunda was a teaching hospital a loud electric bell would sound throughout the building before each delivery. Three rings on the bell would summon a team of students to go out to a call 'on the district', two rings indicated a normal delivery and one ring would alert us to a complication in the labour ward. The ringing of the bell was strictly adhered to. We had all paid the Master of the hospital for our training and the ringing of the bell ensured that we got good value. The labour ward contained five or six beds separated by movable screens, which afforded only the barest privacy. The students and postgraduates would stand on a tiered, wooden gallery and listen to a running commentary from the doctor in charge. With almost four thousand deliveries in 1943 the hospital was a hive of activity. However, it was impossible to ignore the pain and distress of the many women forced to endure long labours without medical help.

Although the value anaesthesia was well known, there were reasons for restricting use of the more effective methods during labour. Injections of morphia derivatives would interfere with the infant's respiratory system. Chloroform could cause the mother to stop breathing and precipitate heart failure. The simplest and safest anaesthetic was the 'rag-and-bottle' variety. We would use this in the hospital and on the district pouring ether on to a mask of layered wire and gauze. Unfortunately, many a mother was almost smothered by doctors trying to ensure adequate pain relief. Concern that the use of anaesthetics could cause maternal and infant deaths was compounded by a number of 'near misses'. Out of a total of 3900 deliveries, ten women and 290 babies died in the Rotunda in 1943. It was no wonder that medical staff were reticent about taking risks.

I finished the course and was appointed Clinical Clerk, supervising deliveries on the district. Memories of earlier days flashed before me as the calls for help came in. Very little had changed in Dublin during the intervening years. People continued to endure overcrowded conditions, on low incomes, with a poor diet and few facilities to encourage hygiene and prevent infection. Somehow the women coped. Many found themselves pregnant almost annually, with no let-up until menopause or death. As Clinical Clerk I found myself presented with the human cost of continual pregnancy. Women would become anaemic and, in the absence of blood transfusions – the National Blood Transfusion Service was not operational until 1948 – could die. The uterus becomes stretched with constant childbearing and many babies would be in the wrong position in the womb. Often the afterbirth would lie in front of the baby, blocking its exit from the womb. Women might haemorrhage after the birth as the uterus would be so floppy as to fail to contract. Ireland's grand multiparas tended to be older women. High blood pressure, with or without bleeding, and eclampsia (convulsions) were killers. They are best prevented by good antenatal care and by limiting births. Doctors would advise women who had survived eclampsia to be careful about starting another baby. For many, living in a country where the laws of both Church and land denied them access to contraception, preventing further pregnancies was impossible. For them pregnancy was to be a death sentence.

Women perceived to be 'at risk' were advised to come into hospital to give birth. This did not prevent many abnormalities occurring on the district, and I would be called out to deal with them or to advise admission to hospital. The Clinical Clerk needed to get to a patient as quickly as possible. This meant having a car, as the hospital did not provide one. My Baby Ford became well known around the north side of Dublin as indicating some emergency and was used as a climbing frame by local children. Complications – forceps deliveries, abnormal positions of the baby, twins and after-birth bleeding – were managed at home. High blood pressure, with or without convulsions, and bleeding before labour required admission. Premature babies were taken to the hospital in shoe-boxes lined with cotton wool.

As the doctors were mostly men, some women preferred to be attended by a midwife. Midwives would call the CC out if they thought there might be a problem. One who found herself delivering twins in a small house in Dublin's North Wall district asked for help. The CC was usually accompanied by a willing postgraduate, but on this occasion it was four o'clock in the morning and I did not want to wake anyone. Setting off alone I reached the house and delivered the second twin. This part was easy enough as the woman had had children before. When she retained the placenta I had to remove it manually. Though this is common practice, I had never done it before and I was terrified. I was on my own, with no student, no hospital, no back-up, just a very assured midwife and a very patient mother.

Any plans for a specialist career required a knowledge of gynaecology – the study of conditions specific to women other than pregnancy. As Ireland's maternity hospitals and relatively small population did not provide enough material, aspiring specialists were forced to look elsewhere. I obtained a year's appointment at the Chelsea Hospital for Women in London. It was 1944, the era of the blackout and the flying bomb. It was here that I heard the subject of contraception freely discussed by colleagues for the first time. I felt far from Dublin.

In 1945 I joined the RAF as a medical officer. Following demobilization in September 1947 I became Registrar at Addenbrooke's Hospital and the County Maternity Hospital in Cambridge. The consultants' operating lists included a number of sterilizations and terminations of pregnancy which I watched. These years were full of new experiences that were to have a marked effect on my thinking and my professional life. It was also in Cambridge that I had my first opportunity to visit a family planning clinic. Friendship with Mollie Lloyd, a journalist who ran the mother and child service in Britain's *Woman's Own* magazine, suggested a whole realm of professional possibilities as she recounted the problems confronting her readers about sex and sex education.

In November 1948 I returned to Dublin and began an appointment as one of the two Assistant Masters at the Rotunda. The workload was tremendous. Lack of education, poverty, poor nutrition, a lack of antenatal care and a high rate of pregnancy contributed to a situation where over my three years as Assistant Master, when 12,010 women were delivered, the abnormal cases admitted to the Rotunda included 1376 assisted forceps births, 687 breech births, 513 cases of bleeding, 700 cases of high blood pressure, 480 infections, 157 instances of syphilis, 76 cases of tuberculosis and 75 occurrences of heart disease. Some 225 women went through labours lasting forty-eight hours or more, occasionally without anaesthesia – epidural was unheard of and there was no resident anaesthetist until 1950. One twenty-six-year-old woman with high blood pressure went blind on her sixth pregnancy only to return pregnant again within a year. Twenty-three women and 800 babies died in those three years. Ten of the mothers who died, one on her nineteenth pregnancy, had never been seen before admission.

Against terrible odds the women accepted their situation with generosity and fortitude. The late Roderick O'Hanlon, Assistant Master at the Rotunda during the 1940s, recalled a poignant example. One woman in the sixth month of her fourth pregnancy was dying from heart disease. O'Hanlon and the Master went along to see her and were greeted by her sister, who jumped up from beside the bed and asked, 'How is she, Doctor?' Struggling for breath the patient said, 'Sir him, Maggie!' She died later that evening leaving her worldly goods of 1s 6d (7 pence) in the care of the hospital porter. One shilling was for a big ice-cream for the Master, and 6d was for a smaller one for Roderick O'Hanlon. She was just one of the many who felt that, even if things had gone wrong, the medical staff had done their best.

TWO

1951 — 1963

Any useful discussion of sex and sexuality requires a non-judgmental approach and the knowledge of some facts. In Ireland this was where the problem lay. Following my time as Assistant Master at the Rotunda I returned home, taking over some rooms in my parents' house in Fitzwilliam Square in November 1951 and setting up in private practice. It was ten years since I had qualified and Ireland had barely changed. While the rest of Europe rebuilt and modernized itself after the ravages of the Second World War, the social and economic picture here had remained virtually static. The importation of contraceptives and the dissemination of information telling people how to use them was still illegal. The calendar 'rhythm method'of family planning was one of the three permitted by both Church and state, the other two relying on cervical mucus (Billing's method) and basal body-temperature changes.

The strict moral guide-lines on sex and sex-related matters that were upheld by the Catholic Church had instilled a fear of sex in many people and created a climate in which it was unlikely that a frank discussion about sex would take place. Although there was no law preventing people from talking about family planning or the use of contraception, for the majority of men and women there was no one to discuss it with. Ireland remained at or near the top of the European table of family size. Advances in medical science were reducing levels of maternal and infant mortality, but poverty, poor nutrition, stress and other problems associated with large families remained.

Throughout his career as a gynaecologist my father, Bethel Solomons, had given advice on methods of birth control to his private patients when they requested it. I pursued the same policy, aware of the injustice of a situation whereby those who had the money could travel outside the state, to the North or to Europe, to obtain contraceptives. There was absolutely nothing one could do to help our public patients. I was also very conscious of a general lack of education about sex. As the Catholic Church and a state which had imbibed the moral teaching of that Church were the major controllers of information about sex, what little the public did know was often factually shaky. As a result of the blanket ban on publishing information about contraception, many books and leaflets on general sex-related subjects were prevented from coming into the country because they contained a chapter or paragraph on family planning. As a result the Irish public was deprived of much enlightening and liberating information.

I had maintained my friendship with Mollie Lloyd, by now one of Britain's leading 'Agony Aunts', writing for *Woman's Own* under the pseudonym 'Ruth Martin'. In 1958 she approached me and asked me to write a chapter describing 'the confinement' for a book she was editing. The book, *Before the Baby and After*, ran to nearly 300 pages and provided a comprehensive guide to childbirth. Unfortunately it was never available in Ireland. The final chapter dealt with family planning and the publishers did not think it was worth distributing in Ireland due to the threat of legal action. In this most insidious and self-censorious way Irish women were denied access to the most innocuous but helpful information about their bodies and reproductive capabilities.

By the mid 1950s Britain had emerged from a period of austerity. As standards of living improved across the water glossy images of new gadgets, fashions and ideas flooded into Ireland in newspapers and magazines. Women's magazines were making a particular impact. Most focused on issues which were deemed to be of interest to women, and this necessarily included contraception and family planning. When an article featuring contraception was brought to the attention of the authorities, the relevant issue would be banned.

In 1951 I met my future wife, Joan Maitland. Joan introduced me to Dr Mary Redding, who had helped to develop the British family planning movement in the years before the war. In 1959 she invited me to sit in on a few sessions at the North Kensington Family Planning Clinic. While there, a telephone call came through to the office and I was ordered to stay. It seemed an unlikely place to be forcibly restrained but I had been kept for an important reason. Joan Rettie, the Secretary of the International Planned Parenthood Federation (IPPF) in Europe, was receiving a growing number of letters from women in Ireland. These women had found the address of the IPPF in women's journals or had obtained it from friends or relations. The letters were varied but were generally from married women, loyal and loving, who were so terrified of further pregnancy that they could not allow their husbands to come near them. Joan Rettie was painfully aware of the despair and anguish faced by these women but could not help them unless they came over to England. When she heard that there was an Irish gynaecologist visiting the Kensington clinic she had instructed, 'Keep him there until I get over.' After our meeting the IPPF gave my name and address to their correspondents and I was able to advise public patients in Mercer's Hospital where I had been appointed Assistant Gynaecologist three years previously. So far as I know, this was the first time public, as opposed to private, patients had access to contraceptive advice.

Listening to the problems of the people who came to see me at Mercer's and hearing the echo of the voices of the many women I had worked with during my career ringing in my ears, I decided that something had to be done. Women were suffering terrible mental, physical and emotional hardship because they had no alternative but to endure unplanned and unwanted pregnancies. Both women and men were suffering due to a lack of basic knowledge about sex. It became clear to me that more people were interested in sex than knew anything about it. I believed that what was needed was a book that explained the basic facts about reproduction, as I was bewildered by the extent of the ignorance that I had encountered amongst my patients. This was particularly obvious where infertility was concerned; it seemed that the problem for a number of people was not infertility but poor technique.

No one in Ireland had written a sex education book before. I decided to write one. To publish anything about sex then required courage. Fortunately Allen Figgis was willing to take the risk and published *Life Cycle* in 1963. Marriage, intercourse, conception, birth, labour, infertility, puberty: all these topics were examined within the pages of the book. There was not, however, a single mention of contraception. *Life Cycle* also contained anatomically correct diagrams of both male and female reproductive organs with a full glossary of terms. Tame stuff now, but *risqué* enough for the Ireland of the early sixties, and the first book to be published on the subject by an Irish author and an Irish publisher.

Life Cycle was well received. There was little adverse reaction and it went into paperback. My daughter, working then in a Dublin bookshop, found that one problem they had was where to place it as their shelves contained no health section. Angela Macnamara, an influential journalist at that time, recommended the book in her 'Questions and Answers' column in the *Irish Press*. Allen Figgis had originally booked space next to Angela Macnamara's column to advertise *Life Cycle,* but when he opened the paper he found that, in later editions, the advert had been stuck at the bottom of the page. Demanding an explanation from the editor, he was told that readers had complained about a book on sex being given so much prominence.

The year 1963 also saw the first issue of *Woman's Way*, the first mass-medium magazine written by Irish women for Irish women. Edited by Caroline Mitchell, her policy was 'hell bent on opening doors and sweeping cobwebs away'. She asked me to contribute occasional articles.

Although we now enjoy greater levels of openness there are still people, young and old, who are denied, or given erroneous, information about sex. It is important that understanding should replace speculation amongst today's sexually active teenagers. Sex education can remove fear, ignorance and embarrassment. It can help to counteract a situation where sex is presented to young people in films, on television and in magazines as a commodity or at best in an idealized setting which promotes unrealistic expectations and can lead to disappointment and distress.

THREE

1963 — 1981

'The middle-aged virgin male is the most deadly and most determined deterrent to the ability of women to grasp the gifts of modern medicine and use them,' Mary Leland wrote in *The Irish Times* in June 1979. By the mid 1960s modern medicine had provided women with the contraceptive pill, the intra-uterine device and the diaphragm. However, while the means existed to control fertility, the Irish state lacked the will to allow it. The Criminal Law (Amendment) Act (1935), Section 17, proscribed the sale of all recognized methods of family planning, and the Censorship of Publications Act (1946), Section 7, prohibited all literature which advocated 'the unnatural prevention of conception'. In 1968 *Humanae Vitae*, a doctrinal statement issued by the Vatican, reiterated the opposition of the Roman Catholic Church to any method of contraception other than 'natural methods'. Members of the Catholic Church's clergy, all of whom had taken a vow of celibacy, ministered to the Irish people on all matters including sex. When it came to the prevention of conception and unwanted pregnancy the Church and the state had the Irish people in a moral and legal stranglehold.

In an article entitled 'Control of Parenthood', published in *The Nation* in December 1921, Dean Inge of St Paul's Cathedral, London said that the level of civilization attained by a nation could be measured by examining the extent to which its nationals practised the use of contraception. If its availability was to be used as a yardstick to measure civilization, then Ireland remained in the Dark Ages.

The sadness of my work 'on the district' and within Dublin's maternity services had convinced me of the need for effective family planning. Several women who came to see me expressed feelings of helplessness and lack of control. A family should not be a burden, but for those who found themselves unable to choose the number of children that they had, it had become precisely that. Too many children led to economic hardship and an inability for people to care for their children as they might wish. Housing problems faced by large families added to parental stress. Meanwhile the health of women coping with successive pregnancies frequently suffered. When these women looked to the medical establishment for help, it was not there.

In 1968 at the Rotunda 5795 babies were born. Only 301 mothers subsequently received family planning advice. One reason for this omission was the belief that the parents of prospective nurses would not want their daughters to train at the Rotunda if they thought the hospital was dispensing advice on contraception. Opposition from the Church could similarly deter patients from attending. Eleanor Holmes, who headed the social work department in the hospital from 1954 until 1987, identified the lack of knowledge about sex and what she called 'the unending pregnancies' as major causes of stress amongst mothers. However, the limited nature of the service at the Rotunda meant that she was able to refer only the 'extreme cases' for family planning advice. Included among these in 1968 were mothers who had tuberculosis or whose children had tuberculosis, those with alcoholic or unemployed husbands and those whose husbands had deserted them during the course of their pregnancy. All of these women had ten or more children.

By the late 1960s issues surrounding family planning had managed to creep on to the national agenda. However, anyone hoping for the dawning of a new age of openness in Ireland was to be sorely disappointed. Church control of teaching in most schools and its influence on government policy ensured that any moves towards providing a greater understanding of 'the facts of life', acceptance of gender equality or of the advantages of limiting family size were doomed. The majority of doctors had been brought up to be practising Catholics and as such often disagreed with the use of contraception. As Dermot Hourihane, now pathologist at St James's Hospital, Dublin, and former Dean of the Medical School at Trinity College, remarked, 'The Irish medical profession was intensely conservative in this respect because of the way it was stitched into the fabric of the establishment.'

Unlike the majority of Irish people, I am Jewish and look to my own faith to provide me with ethical and spiritual guidance. Orthodox Jewish teaching encourages large families but permits the use of the pill, the diaphragm, and the intra-uterine device. Any methods that prevent spermatozoa (male seed) from entering the vagina – the condom and withdrawal – are forbidden. I, however, follow Liberal Jewish doctrine, which is not so restrictive and allows me to advise any method of contraception without implying any break-away from my religion.

In 1964, the mainstream Protestant Churches, including those represented in Ireland, gradually adopted the use of contraception as ethically acceptable for Christians. The World Council of Churches had concluded in 1959 that there is 'no moral difference between the use of the infertile period, artificial barriers to the meeting of sperm and ovum, and drugs regulating ovulation'.

As a young man I had listened to my father's indignant reaction when a local chemist, Rosenthal of Merrion Row, was visited by Gardaí, fined and threatened with closure if he continued to sell condoms. My father paid the fine. In 1968 little had changed. The sale, importation and advertisement of contraceptives remained illegal. Books and periodicals advising the 'unnatural prevention of conception' were banned as being 'indecent or obscene'. Contraceptives were intercepted and confiscated by customs as they entered the country, and Irish booksellers risked financial loss if in error they stocked items on the 'banned' or 'to be banned' list.

10 December 1966 was United Nations Human Rights Day. Activities concluded with a declaration on family planning and population growth by twelve international heads of state. 'We believe', they said, 'that the great majority of parents desire to have the knowledge and the means to plan their families; that the opportunity to decide the number and spacing of children is a basic human right.' In 1967 the National Health Service (Family Planning) Act enabled local health authorities in England and Wales to provide a family planning service for all those who wanted one. At the United Nations International Conference on Human Rights in Tehran in 1968 fifty-six nations, including the Holy See, voted for a resolution which considered 'that couples have a basic human right to decide freely on the number and spacing of their children and a right to adequate education and information in this respect'.

In Ireland, meanwhile, nobody was saying much about human rights in relaton to contraception. Pharmaceutical companies had managed to introduce the contraceptive pill to Ireland in 1963 as a 'cycle regulator'. It was not until years later that they followed the advice of Dr John O'Connell, then editor of *The Irish Medical Times,* urging them to come out of the closet and advertise 'the pill' as a contraceptive. Many thousands of Irish women became usefully aware of their menstrual irregularity.

In March 1968 I received a telephone call from James Loughran, a general practitioner in Skerries. He asked if I would be interested in attending a meeting on family planning that he was arranging with Joan Wilson, another GP. James Loughran said that he had contacted me because I was the only gynaecologist in Ireland who he knew advised the use of contraception. I went along to the meeting in Buswell's Hotel, Dublin, eager and interested. There were eight of us at this, the first of a series of meetings that was to lead over the next eleven months to the establishment of the Republic's first family planning clinic.

Most of the eight original members of this embryo Irish family planning movement had a medical background. James Loughran had qualified as a doctor at University College Dublin before spending time in London hospitals. He held a passionate and often controversial belief in the value of contraception. Joan Wilson had found that as a doctor in general practice in Ireland she had been unable to help the many women who came begging her to help them prevent further pregnancies. She claimed that 'the average GP was as much use to the average patient as the milkman'. Social worker Yvonne Pim had learned through personal experience that she had to leave the state if she wanted to obtain contraception. Joan and Yvonne had embarked on a series of sex education talks in Protestant secondary schools in Dublin, becoming affectionately known as 'the sex ladies'. Robert Towers was also a doctor and a Catholic. As editor of *The Irish Medical Times* he emphasized the need for family planning and birth control. As a pathologist in London Dermot Hourihane had done voluntary work for the Catholic Marriage Advisory Service and had encouraged the use of the rhythm method. He had become disillusioned when too many women became pregnant too often. Both Towers and Hourihane risked far more than any of us by opposing mainstream opinion.

Máire Mullarney was without doubt the most unusual member of the gang of eight. A qualified physiotherapist and a state-registered nurse, she was a practising and convinced Catholic. Máire was a member of the Irish Theological Society and the mother of eleven children. As one for whom 'natural' methods of family planning had clearly failed, Máire's conversion had come when she visited a family planning clinic in Portugal and learned more about the subject. The last member of the eight was invaluable and unique. A moral theologian at a Jesuit college, he was prepared to infuse our manoeuvrings with his knowledge of Catholic doctrine coupled with advice and encouragement. In return we guaranteed him strict anonymity.

All eight of us believed that the prohibition of effective family planning was wrong. The 'natural method' permitted by the Church was unreliable.

With the rhythm method sex is restricted to those days each month when pregnancy is least likely to occur. Most women shed an egg (ovum) from the ovary two weeks before the next menstrual period is due. This egg survives for two to three days and can be fertilized during this time. Spermatozoa, from the man, have a similarly short lifespan. Intercourse within two to three days before and after ovulation, or 'the fertile period', as it is sometimes called, must be avoided if pregnancy is to be prevented. However, calculation of this fertile period is difficult if periods are irregular. Keeping a daily temperature chart is useful as a slight rise in a woman's temperature can coincide with ovulation. Changes in the vaginal mucus also indicate ovulation. While the rhythm method is ideal for couples who have objections to other methods of contraception and a high level of self-control, it is not so ideal for the rest of us. Taking temperatures and observing your vaginal mucus can be inconvenient, distasteful and sometimes misleading. A couple's sex drive can override the need to avoid intercourse over a period that sometimes extends beyond seven days. I have had a number of patients tell me that using the rhythm method literally ruined their sex life and damaged their marriage. Men and women can find the method frustrating and can become irritable and depressed. The rhythm method has a failure rate of between 10 and 20 per cent.

Unable to obtain, or unwilling to use, other methods, many couples practised coitus interruptus, which involves the withdrawal of the penis from the vagina before ejaculation. The only trouble is that its success in preventing pregnancy is severely limited. Sperm can be emitted from the penis prior to ejaculation and some men find that they lack sufficient self-control to withdraw in time. Women can also find this method frustrating. Withdrawal has a failure rate of some 20 per cent.

The 'artificial' methods have a lower failure rate: the 'pill' less than 1 per cent; diaphragm, or cap, 3–5 per cent; intrauterine device 1–3 per cent; and the condom 5 per cent. Choice of the first three depends on the user's preference and suitability as determined by a doctor; regular check-ups are required to ensure efficiency and deal with the infrequent but possible side-effects or complications. One major advantage is that these allow a woman to control her fertility without having to depend on her partner.

Once we had established that all eight members of the group possessed a common aim, we set about discussing the problems, legal and otherwise, that would confront our organization as we attempted to make 'unnatural' means of family planning available to the Irish people. We formed a study group and we invited selected members of the legal and medical professions amongst others to join the meetings. As a Professor of Moral Theology at Maynooth, Dr Denis O'Callaghan's willingness to contribute to the group was a great tonic. Addressing us on 'The Morality of Contraception' he demonstrated a degree of tolerance unusual among Church dignitaries. 'The Church's infallibility cannot be involved in family planning. If continence is impractical for medical or family reasons, more effective methods are reasonable,' he informed us.

I had maintained my correspondence with the International Planned Parenthood Federation (IPPF) during the sixties and in May 1968 I found myself writing enthusiastically to Joan Rettie. 'Hold your breath,' I wrote, 'there is more than a glimmer of light suggesting that there might well be some sort of break-through for family planning of a reliable nature in this country. Will you tell us how we should progress from the present small beginnings to potential involvement of the whole country? Recently the large majority of the patients attending the family planning clinic at the Coombe Hospital refused to hear any more about rhythm methods and insisted on the pill or nothing. The clinic had to be closed. While the other two Dublin maternity hospitals are equally conservative, the senior social worker at the Rotunda is very interested and will attend meetings in future. Would you consider sending one of your staff to advise?'

Philip Kestelman, the secretary to the IPPF European Regional Medical Committee, came to meet us in June while his wife visited her parents in Limerick. Thankfully he reported back favourably to Joan Rettie, saying that he found us most professional. Rettie had been involved with the problems of establishing national family planning movements since 1956. In August 1968 she came to see us in Dublin. From then on the IPPF gave us financial support starting with a grant of £1000. On her return to London Rettie sent us a long letter detailing the steps she thought we should take before setting up the clinic. Find a leading barrister and ask him for a legal opinion, she advised. We had to know if setting up a family planning clinic in Ireland would contravene the law.

Noel Peart, Senior Counsel, was our choice. A successful barrister, Peart was an officer in the Order of the Knights of Malta and a popular contributor to 'Question Time', a programme on national radio. On 4 October 1968 he sent us his opinion, and refused to charge us a fee.

'It is not illegal to set up a Family Planning Clinic,' was Peart's conclusion. 'Unless the Clinic contravenes some other principle of law, it is clearly legitimate to offer medical advice upon the desirability of, and the method of employment of, indicated contraceptive methods, in particular cases.' The clinic must 'accept absolutely that it cannot sell contraceptives', said Peart. 'If contraceptives are going to be provided for the clientele, they will have to be provided free of charge.' Peart acknowledged that there would be a difficulty if the clinic wished to advertise its services because of the restrictions placed on information about contraception by the Censorship of Publications Act (1946): 'One can hardly close one's eyes to the fact that a family planning clinic in Dublin is likely to meet with strong opposition, particularly from clerical sources.' However, he concluded that 'as long as the Clinic acts with discretion and does not openly challenge prosecution no prosecution would be instituted'. Finally he recommended that we form ourselves into a company to prevent any possible prosecution of individual members.

The study group continued to meet until February 1969, planning the clinic and other developments such as how we would go about training doctors, nurses and lay workers. We had to establish a means of supply if we wanted to issue contraceptives to our clients. In order to pay for all this we had to prepare a budget submission for the IPPF. The IPPF was to fund the clinic on a continuing basis. The rest of the money that we got came from voluntary subscriptions and philanthropic donors and organizations like the American Ford Foundation.

Although several solicitors who were approached refused to act for the group, Raymond Downey took up the gauntlet and proceeded to try and find suitable premises for the clinic. We were clear about what we wanted. It had to be somewhere close to the city centre and a bus stop and in a row of houses in order to avoid attracting attention to clients who would be ringing the bell. The premises had to be on the ground floor with a telephone, toilet and washbasin, and with space for consulting and reception/waiting-rooms. Landlords may have wanted tenants but the mere mention of contraception put them off. This delayed progress for several weeks until suitable premises and a willing landlord were found at 10 Merrion Square. We were able to rent two ground-floor rooms in a five-storey Georgian house whose proximity to the Dáil, the National Museum and the National Maternity Hospital, while unintentional, did seem appropriate. A way out of the house through the back garden into an adjoining lane for use in the event of a possible raid was an added attraction.

With advice from Christopher Morris, an architect who had joined the study group, the necessary alterations were made to the building and we were able to hold our first committee meeting there on 18 February 1969. It felt like graduation day. Top of the agenda was the issue of a name for the new company. The name would have to express our aims clearly without risking our existence. As we planned to advise on infertility as well as contraception we found it appropriate to choose 'The Fertility Guidance Company Limited'. A brass plaque was soon fixed to the front door, inscribed 'Fertility Guidance Company', giving our telephone number and hours of opening. By 20 March the company had been legally formed. The 'subscribers' in the Articles of Association were James Loughran, Joan Wilson, Robert Towers, Máire Mullarney, Dermot Hourihane, Yvonne Pim and myself.

Although the company was formally formed only in March, we had been operating a service since 25 February. One of the four doctors, myself, Loughran, Wilson or the late Anne Legge, an early supporter, took it in turns to attend the one-hour sessions on Tuesday and Friday evenings. We were joined by Mullarney, Pim and two enthusiastic lay workers, Nora O'Laoghaire and Betty Young. Our main fear was not being raided by the Gardaí but that the phone would not ring. In fact only 167 new patients visited the clinic in 1969, and we spent most evenings chatting and drinking cups of tea. Here lay the rub. It was a difficult business putting the word about that a family planning clinic had set up shop in Dublin. We had agreed during meetings that we should keep a low profile in order to avoid possible legal challenge. We were relying on discreet disclosures from doctors, nurses and between friends to alert people to our existence.

In the early days patients must have wondered what was

going to happen to them when they rang our doorbell. Some had a friend in tow to give them moral support, a few asked if they had to see a priest, all needed help and practical information. Hopefully this is what they got. It was the lay workers' job to put them at their ease and it was the doctors' to see that they were given the advice and information they wanted. We told clients about all methods of contraception that were available to us at the time; this included the rhythm method, the pill and diaphragms. It was then up to the client to make up her mind. At this time the majority were middle-class. We regretted that the so-called 'blue card' holders, the majority of whom were working-class, were not turning up to any great extent. It revealed a problem with our information networks and customer targeting practices but it also revealed the extent to which conservative teaching continued to dominate people's lives. Even in 1969 the majority of Irish people would have been unwilling to visit a family planning clinic, believing the use of 'unnatural' methods of family planning to be a sin.

We did not sit around twiddling our thumbs for long. Public interest in the clinic was growing. A number of articles about it had appeared in newspapers and magazines and two members of staff had been interviewed on national radio. Women's groups wrote to us requesting that we send a speaker. As more people discovered our existence the number attending the clinic steadily increased. Some general practitioners and hospital consultants, while unwilling to join us, began to refer those patients who could not or would not take the pill. Some women were unable to take the pill for medical reasons, others refused to take it, as they held the unsubstantiated belief that the pill was abortifacient. The Church's condemnation of the pill as a method of contraception unnerved some Catholics, who felt unable to take it.

By the end of 1970 we were holding six clinics a week and averaging ten patients per session. We had acquired eleven doctors including another gynaecologist, Rosemary Jordan, sixteen lay workers, an extra nurse, a financial administrator, a waiting list of three to four weeks, and had seen 1180 new patients. The contributions we received from some of our patients for advice made nominal payment of staff a possibility for the first time and we were looking for premises in order to open up a second clinic.

As our worries about attracting sufficient numbers of clients subsided, worries about obtaining adequate supplies of contraceptives surfaced. The only reliable method of contraception that was legally available was the pill. In an attempt to overcome this obstacle we arranged with the IPPF for delivery of contraceptives by mail order. Patients ordered condoms, spermicides and diaphragms on forms provided by the clinic. Small flat packages carrying hand-written addresses usually got past the staff in the cross-channel sorting offices. Larger packages containing spermicides were sometimes intercepted by customs officials. Any member of the clinic staff, their friends, relations and supporters who were travelling to England, had their suitcases commandeered and were ordered to bring back contraceptives. My mother and my mother-in-law, who were both in their late seventies, took great pleasure in acting as 'contraceptive couriers', secretly hoping that they would be challenged.

Joyce Neill, Chairwoman of the Northern Ireland Family Planning Association, helped us out by arranging that doctors who were sympathetic to our aims and lived near the border would drive across into Donegal and post supplies to us in Dublin. These supplies generally consisted of spermicidal jelly or cream required for use with diaphragms. Everyone who helped was aware that they were risking penalties and embarrassment, but we were never without supplies for long and as an emergency measure could always advise the use of Maclean's children's toothpaste as its potentially spermicidal properties were then recognized by the IPPF. Joyce Neill also trained some of our nurses and lay workers and fitted patients we referred North with intra-uterine devices. At the time we were unable to offer this service at the clinic as it was a controversial method of contraception.

There had been a great deal of talk about the IUD being abortifacient. The IUD has a minor irritating effect on the lining of the uterus which stops any fertilized egg from embedding into the uterine wall. It takes four to five days for a fertilized egg to travel from its origin in the Fallopian tube to complete embedding. Many fail to do so of their own accord, and are expelled during the next menstrual period. The belief that life begins from the moment of fertilization, and thus anything preventing its progression is abortifacient, is common. I believe that a fertilized egg only becomes a pregnancy when it has embedded into the wall of the uterus, and I do not consider that the IUD works by causing abortion. This controversy over the definition of the IUD was to take on a greater significance during the O'Reilly case and during future wranglings with the Irish Medical Association.

The Irish Medical Union had begun to take an interest in the issues surrounding birth control. In November 1970 the union held a discussion, 'Family planning, the doctor's dilemma', at the Shelbourne Hotel. The panel consisted of the clinic's continuing supporter Professor Denis O'Callaghan, Senator Mary Bourke, who had a specialized knowledge of constitutional law, and Brendan Murphy and Eamon O'Dwyer, two consultant gynaecologists who were strong advocates of natural methods of family planning. I was also on the panel. There was a capacity audience, and if the meeting proved anything it was that consensus would be hard to find.

The laws of the land remained static but the family planning movement pressed on. In 1971 The Fertility Guidance Company opened its second clinic at 15 Mountjoy Square. The clinic was in a more socially deprived area than Merrion Square. Close to the Rotunda, the new building provided us with much-needed extra space for patients, administration, committee meetings and a library. Any alteration in the laws governing contraception 'which would change the environment of the country which we all find a help to be good and virtuous' was to be avoided, Father Denis Faul of St Patrick's Academy, Dungannon, told delegates at a Christus Rex conference in Bundoran in April 1971.

The battle-lines were being drawn. On 22 May 1971 members of the Irish Women's Liberation Movement travelled to Belfast on what became known as 'the contraceptive train'. The women bought condoms and other contraceptives in Belfast and returned with their illegal imports to challenge the customs officials at the Dublin terminus. The authorities let them pass without question. As a media event the contraceptive train was a great success. Highlighting the fact that in some respects Irish law was an ass, the women got huge press coverage.

Staff in the clinics at Merrion and Mountjoy Square had been relying on colleagues in the North to fit their patients with IUDs. This was to change. David Nowlan had returned home in the late 1960s after working as a Government Medical Officer in Jamaica to find that in Ireland the use of contraception carried tougher penalties than those incurred by prostitution. He had been fitting IUDs for women in Jamaica and could not understand why we were sending women to Belfast to get 'accidentally bombed or shot' when we could fit them in the clinic. Joyce Neill came down from Belfast to give us a talk and demonstration, and by September 1970 we were inserting IUDs at Mountjoy Square. By the end of that year we had fitted almost two hundred.

In 1970 I was invited by two professors at Trinity College to lecture on family planning to medical students as part of their pharmacology and physiology courses. It was the first time that an Irish medical school had included the subject as a part of the curriculum. The interest shown by the students confirmed that there was an urgent need for information. If this need existed in a Dublin medical school then how much more so in the general population. Mary Bourke was continuing her struggle to achieve legislative reform in the Senate. In July 1971 she attempted, with Senators John Horgan and Trevor West, to introduce a bill to amend the Acts preventing the sale and import of contraceptives and the Acts which prohibited the publication of information about contraception. The bill was not only refused a reading it was denied publication.

Despite this set-back, we were consolidating our position as a reputable, efficient and ecumenical body. William O'Dwyer, a consultant physician, surgeon Patrick Collins, and two consultant gynaecologists became members of the company. William O'Dwyer specialized in kidney disease. Sometimes this can be aggravated by pregnancy and thus pregnancy should be avoided. He was deeply concerned to find himself prevented by the law from giving his patients life-saving advice. George Henry, later to become Master at the Rotunda, and Roderick O'Hanlon strengthened our team and provided us with access to two more hospitals for investigation of cases of infertility whenever the need arose.

Family Planning – A Guide for Parents and Prospective Parents was published in December 1971. Written by three members of the education committee, Loughran, Nowlan and Towers, it sold over 800 copies in the first month of publication. Such was the demand for the guide that two further editions and thousands of copies were distributed over the next five years. It was not until 1976 that the guide was to become seriously controversial. The Rotunda became the first Irish maternity hospital to set up a family planning clinic in 1972. Sessions were held twice a week and patients were either prescribed the pill, given advice on rhythm methods or referred to the Fertility Guidance Company if the patient expressed a desire for a diaphragm or IUD. Seven hundred and eighty patients were seen at the Rotunda clinic in 1972. At least one hospital was getting the message. With a family planning service available in a state-supported hospital, the government's retention of legal status quo *vis-à-vis* contraception seemed hypocritical.

Irish legal and constitutional history was to be made that year. Mrs Mary McGee was twenty-nine and lived in a mobile home with her fisherman husband and their four children. Each of her pregnancies had been complicated by high blood pressure. On one occasion this had been the cause of temporary paralysis. Mrs McGee had been advised against having any more children. Fitted with a diaphragm by James Loughran, she had ordered a packet of spermicide by mail order from England. When the package was intercepted and confiscated by customs, Loughran and his solicitor encouraged Mrs McGee to take legal action against the state on the grounds that the Criminal Law Amendment Act (1935), which prohibited the importation of contraceptives, was inconsistent with that section of the 1937 Constitution which respects the rights of each individual citizen. The case, which was taken against the Attorney General and the Revenue Commissioners, was dismissed by the High Court in July. This was not the end of the affair. Mrs McGee pursued the case by making an appeal to the Supreme Court, and in November 1973 the High Court judgment was reversed by a majority of four to one.

Encouraged by the result of the McGee case, which it was believed would accelerate government action, and by a change of government from Fianna Fáil to a Fine Gael/Labour coalition, I made a personal approach to Patrick Cooney, Minister for Justice. During this half-hour interview I reminded him of the risks to health and the pressure on housing, education and employment that came with uncontrolled pregnancies. Stressing the work undertaken by the Fertility Guidance Company, I put the case for a national family planning service that was flexible enough to meet the needs of all Irish citizens according to their personal beliefs. Patrick Cooney listened, and said he already had plans for improving the legislation.

The clinics meanwhile continued to see a number of low-income patients who were entitled to free medical treatment. In theory free treatment meant that the state met the cost of medical, hospital and drug services required by the patient; in practice the government said that family planning services and contraceptives were not covered by the free treatment scheme. They refused to pay us. In July 1973 we changed the company's name to the 'Irish Family Planning Association Limited'. We asked the Department of Industry and Commerce if we could drop the 'Ltd' and thereby qualify for charitable status. They refused. Despite the fact that we were providing a service free of charge to those who could not afford to pay for it, and despite the fact that, at her request, we were supplying Dr Allene Scott of the National Drugs Advisory Board with information about any adverse reactions to oral contraceptives, they said that we did not satisfy a charitable or scientific function. Fortunately the IPPF soon elected the Irish Family Planning Association as an associate member. We were now entitled to receive grants and to attend meetings of the European Regional Council. Grants were essential for our survival. Donations received from our patients for advice did not meet the running expenses of rented premises and the staff, mainly part-time, who were paid on a sessional basis. The IFPA now employed fifteen doctors, seven nurses, twenty-five lay workers, a social worker, a clinic secretary and an administrator.

In November 1973 Mary Robinson (*née* Bourke), Trevor West and John Horgan tried again and introduced their second Family Planning Bill to the Senate. It included new proposals – jurisdiction over the provision of contraceptives should pass from the Minister for Justice to the Minister for Health, and the Censorship Acts should be amended. Unlike the Senators' earlier attempt, the bill did succeed in getting a first reading. The Church reacted negatively. The Hierarchy issued a statement to the press warning against any move to legalize the sale of contraceptives in Ireland.

The Most Reverend Dr Daly, Bishop of Ardagh and Clonmacnoise, spoke to the Irish people on Radio Eireann calling the potential introduction of legal birth control 'a calamity' and advising legislators 'to form a conscientious judgment on moral issues'. Dr John O'Connell TD quickly reacted with criticism of the Hierarchy for what he called 'this subtle form of intimidation'.

Andrew Rynne, an extrovert general practitioner with surgical experience, had now joined the IFPA. In February 1974 he became the first Irishman to perform a vasectomy in Ireland by performing what was to be the first of many such operations at the clinic in Mountjoy Square. As with tubal ligation in women, this method of sterilization for men is virtually 100 per cent successful.

A temporary set-back with an element of farce followed during the same month. The IFPA and a similar company, Family Planning Services, were summoned to court by the Attorney General. We were to answer allegations that we had sold, offered and advertised contraceptives. We were also to face charges relating to the distribution of the Loughran, Nowlan and Towers *Guide to Family Planning* which had been originally published three years earlier.

The court case resulted from a complaint made to the authorities by John O'Reilly of the Irish Family League. He had ordered and obtained by post condoms and a booklet on family planning. The two letters had been signed, on his instruction, by his two daughters aged eleven and nine. The matter was reported to the Attorney General. On the day of the hearing the court-room was filled to capacity. Lawyers, journalists, doctors, gardaí, social workers, the staff and supporters of both defendant organizations were squashed together on hard benches. The defence was happily so clear-cut that District Justice Kearney dismissed all charges.

A lively debate in the Senate which followed the second reading of Mary Robinson's bill was curtailed when Patrick Cooney, the Minister for Justice, announced that the

Coalition government would be introducing its own bill. The bill was to be called 'The Control of Importation, Sale and Manufacture of Contraceptives Bill (1974), and it brought mayhem and fiasco to the Dáil in July. A free vote on the bill had been agreed. Whilst the debate around the introduction of the bill was infused from time to time with a measure of common sense, many of the speakers reiterated the intransigent views of the Hierarchy that the use of contraception was immoral and could lead to the collapse of civilization as we know it. Oliver J. Flanagan, a member of the Coalition government for Laois/Offaly, during two hours of bluff and histrionics, envisaged 'dangers from sex speculators and legalized brothels, with an increase in deserted wives and alcoholism'. It was not only Flanagan's performance that pointed to the way the government had decided to vote. Liam Cosgrave, the leader of the Coalition, went through the 'No' lobby, to be followed by Richard Burke, the Minister for Education, and five other members of the party, effectively ensuring the defeat of their own bill. Conservatism had triumphed and the Irish Family League pickets standing outside the Dáil celebrated.

As politicians debated, family planning groups and members of the public moved on. The IFPA opened a new clinic in a terraced house in Synge Street close to the birthplace of George Bernard Shaw. We felt that a clinic in this area would suit more patients and would provide a replacement to Merrion Square, which had become too small and was to be sold. Requests from women's groups and medical organizations for us to provide speakers for their meetings continued to pour in. They wanted to know about all methods of contraception and about the availability of sterilization. Despite the absence of any legal restriction, sterilization operations had never been easy to come by in Ireland. George Henry, Chairman of the IFPA Medical Committee, provided an exception, doing female sterilizations at his Dublin hospital, but his waiting list was out of control and he could not take any more patients.

I performed very few tubal ligations as I was conscious that many of my nursing staff had ethical objections to the procedure. I had too much regard for their profession to ignore their beliefs. Whether or not a doctor was able to perform this operation was a lottery, depending on the hospital in which one worked. The matron and the theatre sisters in Baggot Street Hospital came up with a solution. 'Ask the parish priest,' they said. 'If he approves we'll have no objection and we'll get two nurses who are willing to assist you.' It was a different story at Mercer's Hospital, where the otherwise co-operative theatre sister stated, 'You are not going to do that in my theatre.' George Henry and, later, Edgar Ritchie in Cork were the only gynaecologists attached to hospitals where no objections were raised, hence their long waiting lists. At the Rotunda, considered one of the more liberal hospitals, patients who wanted to be sterilized after giving birth to seven or more children, or enduring a number of Caesarean sections, had to be stringently assessed by an 'ethics committee'.

Throughout 1974 our newly formed Education and Information Committee played an active part in the Association's development. Ignorance in sexual matters was damaging the sex lives of the Irish people. Sex should be enjoyable. For many people it was just plain frightening. Despite censorship and religious and political restrictions, two seminars for public health nurses brought seventy people the following year to Mountjoy Square. Forty general practitioners attended our first training course on 'family planning for doctors'. By 1992, 850 doctors and 680 nurses have received certificates of proficiency from the IFPA or the Irish College of General Practitioners and the Institute of Obstetricians and Gynaecologists.

Cork got its first family planning clinic in 1974. Edgar Ritchie had worked as a specialist obstetrician in Africa. He had become an expert in the management of the emergencies associated with inadequate antenatal care and the absence of control over fertility. Returning to Ireland he was amazed that there were no family planning facilities in Cork. In a letter to the IPPF he had outlined his interest in setting up some sort of facility. They put him in touch with us and the clinic in Tuckey Street was opened and has never looked back.

Rumblings of trouble within our organization began to surface during a meeting in November 1975 of the newly formed Finance Committee, of which I was the chairman. The company's accountant, David Ennis, made it clear to us that there were a number of financial irregularities in the company books and that as our income had now reached six figures we needed expert guidance. Following investigation it transpired that £10,000 had been paid for goods for the clinic that had never arrived. Blank cheques had been signed on a regular basis. In April 1976 we discovered that we had made a further payment of £2600 for supplies that were never delivered. Ennis told us that he had no intention of finalizing the accounts until there had been a thorough investigation. The relevant member of staff was identified and relinquished her position.

The disclosures sent shock waves through the Finance and Executive Committees. At a special meeting on 21 May 1976 fifty-two members met the company's solicitor and accountant to try and resolve the mess. The mood at the meeting was hostile. People pointed out faults in the structure of the company and, whilst I was not held responsible in any way, some called unsuccessfully for the resignation of both the Company Chairman and the Company Secretary. The press understandably drew attention to our problems. While *Hibernia* printed a fair investigative article headed simply, 'The Clinic's Missing Money', another piece in *The Catholic Herald*, titled 'Scandal Rocks Pill Clinics', alleged that the money had been embezzled by a supporter of republicanism and that we were backing abortion. The age of the amateur administrator was truly dead. From now on we were to enlist the services of professionals.

Awareness of the benefits of birth control was growing.

The opening of another family planning clinic in Galway was welcomed by the IFPA and we were heartened by plans for a clinic in Limerick. It was the calm before the storm.

On 24 November 1976 the Censorship of Publications Board imposed a ban on the IFPA *Guide to Family Planning*. The booklet had been published in 1971 and was now in its second edition. We were astonished by the move. We were also somewhat perplexed to find out that the booklet had been banned because the Board considered it to be 'indecent or obscene' and not because it 'advocated the unnatural use of contraception'. In 1974 Justice Kearney had dismissed a similar action in the District Court. It seemed like a sick joke; nevertheless the book was removed from circulation and Irish people were denied access to this clear, concise guide to reproduction, sex and contraception.

George Henry, now Chairman of the IFPA, issued a statement on 6 December. He said that lawyers had been instructed to prepare a case challenging the ban. The ban was seriously affecting the service provided in the clinics, he told reporters, and there was a large number of people wishing to order the booklet by post. 'No Sex Please' was the headline in *The Irish Times* the next day. 'Absurd – not Obscene' commented *Hibernia*. With the expense of a hearing in the Supreme Court looming, the IFPA set up an appeal fund headed by three public figures: Victor Bewley, Maurice Dockrell TD and Senator Evelyn Owens. Bewley was irritated that the state was once again meddling with people's personal choices. 'There are people in this country who do not want this information and that is their affair. But there is a considerable number of other people who do want family planning advice and they are entitled to it,' said Bewley. 'I'm past it but I'm for it,' declared Dockrell. Family planning legislation was part of liberal thought, liberal government and civilized life, he said.

The court action was taken jointly by the IFPA and Joan

Wilson, who was on the Executive Committee at the time, against the Attorney General and the State. Family Planning Services brought a separate but similar action. The case was originally heard in May before Mr Justice Hamilton but judgment was deferred. When it came back into the court on 1 July Justice Hamilton ruled that the ban was invalid and awarded costs to the IFPA. The Attorney General appealed but the ruling stood and the booklet became available to the public again. Sadly, radio, television and press coverage during the trial revealed that the Irish state was not exactly teetering on the brink of liberal conversion.

Meanwhile the IFPA had adopted a more professional administrative approach. Robert (Bobbie) Law, previously head of the Work Study Department at Guinness's, was appointed Director of Administration and Company Secretary, and the Finance Committee was enlarged. The financial fracas of 1976 and 1977 had taken its toll and despite being proposed for re-election as Chairman of the committee I was happy to step down. The time had also come to let another doctor take my place at the clinics and become a member of the Executive Committee. I had been involved in the Association since 1969 and was pleased to note that during my final year of active involvement the clinics had seen more than 7200 new patients. Twenty-three doctors, eleven of whom were women, fourteen nurses and fifteen lay workers staffed the clinics.

Fianna Fáil were returned to power in June 1977. They proceeded to form a government and Charles Haughey was appointed Minister for Health. Haughey began his tenure as Minister by inviting two representatives from each of the country's eight health boards along to a meeting to discuss the formulation of a new family planning bill. He also met representatives of the Irish Medical Association and the IFPA. The IFPA found themselves in the invidious position of having to counter opposition to a bill that was not yet published. It was a strange situation but one that would become commonplace in future Irish political life.

Haughey's Health (Family Planning) Bill was published on 13 December 1978. Those of us who had hoped for something progressive and workable studied it in dismay. Although the bill incorporated much of Mary Robinson's rejected proposals of 1973 and some amendments to the existing censorship and contraceptive laws, it left a lot to be desired. The contents, which were listed in seventeen complex sections, included the designation of responsibility to the health boards for the provision of a national 'natural' family planning service. Contraceptives were to be available only on prescription and prescriptions would be given only to people who were married. Doctors who handed out these prescriptions were duty bound to provide a service for those requesting advice on 'natural' family planning. The commercial importation of contraceptives was to be restricted by licence to wholesale agents and chemists' shops. Chemists objecting to the use of contraceptives would not be under any obligation to stock them.

The Hierarchy may have been pleased but we in the family planning movement were not. The health boards had never actually agreed to provide any sort of service. Some chemists might not agree to stock contraceptives and this would leave people in one-chemist towns and villages high and dry. Many doctors who were already providing a family planning service objected to the imposition of health board control. They were also concerned about invading the privacy of their clients by being required by law to ask if the patient were married or not. The clinics were worried. We feared that we might have to close if we could no longer provide contraceptives. The problem could be overcome only if an amendment was introduced allowing the clinics to open up a chemist's shop on their premises.

A family planning clinic without contraceptives is like a pub with no beer, as one of our supporters pointed out during the campaign to try and highlight the potential effects of the bill. 'Phone Your TD Today' posters were plastered around cities and towns in an attempt to encourage our supporters to put pressure on their public representatives to amend the bill and prevent the closure of the clinics. Whatever influence all this frenetic activity had is hard to judge but the Minister did introduce the amendment when the bill finally became operative in November 1980. The IFPA still had to apply to the new Minister, Michael Woods, for a licence to operate the clinics. This was granted but it remained illegal to sell contraceptives there. To get over this problem we had to set up a chemist's shop and, despite the expense, this was added to the new premises at the clinic that we had opened in August 1979 in Cathal Brugha Street.

The legislation was still restrictive. Three years later Andrew Rynne would be fined £500 for supplying condoms to a patient. He had done so at the weekend when the chemists' shops were closed. The fine was later lifted by Judge Frank Roe, who told the nation, 'Anyone without condoms at the weekend will have to wait until Monday.' Condoms have been used for hundreds, perhaps thousands of years. In 1992 a nineteenth-century French condom was sold in London for $6300. It is a very simple form of contraception. The man, or his partner, merely places the condom over the erect penis before there is any foreplay or penetration. It is removed after intercourse and disposed of. Among experienced users the condom has a 5 per cent failure rate. In 1985 there was some relaxation in government policy and condoms became available to anyone over eighteen. There was no need for a prescription. In 1990 the IFPA were fined £400 for selling condoms illegally in the Virgin Megastore in Dublin. When the company appealed, the fine was increased to £500.

Department of Health figures released in May 1992 showed that 108 people have already died in Ireland because of AIDS, the total number affected being 272, with 70 new cases under treatment. According to Fiona Mulcahy, senior consultant in Genito-Urinary Medicine at St James's Hospital, Dublin, there were 2244 new cases of sexually transmitted diseases between 1987 and 1991. It is

Five founder-members of the Irish Family Planning Association (Michael Solomons, Yvonne Pim, Robert Towers, Joan Wilson and Máire Mullarney) at the tenth-anniversary celebrations in the Tara Towers Hotel, Dublin, 11 October 1979

Joan Rettie, George Henry and Margaret Towers at the same event.

known that, used correctly, condoms can reduce the risk of transmission of the HIV virus which can lead to AIDS as well as reducing the risk of other sexually transmitted diseases. Condoms have become more important because of this dual role. Liberal changes in the laws with respect to the sale of condoms have been resisted by the Church and conservative political groupings like the SPUC, PLAC and the Irish Family League; but as a result of the recent Health (Family Planning) Amendment Bill condoms may now be sold in any retail outlet supervised by a person aged over eighteen to everyone aged over seventeen, irrespective of marital status and without a medical prescription. Many outlets refuse to stock them; vending machines are forbidden. It is interesting to note that a couple may legally marry within the state at the age of sixteen, but may not use a condom until they are a year older.

Before the introduction of new family planning legislation in 1980 another debate began within the ranks of the Irish medical profession. 'The IUD is not a contraceptive' was among the motions tabled for the Annual General Meeting of the Irish Medical Association at Ennis in April 1979. The Central Council of the IMA had recommended that the motion be included as they felt that it impacted on Section 10 of the new Health Act, which reiterated the legal prohibition of abortion in Ireland. I was concerned about the motivation of the IMA. I was also worried about the implications for patients and the IFPA if the motion were passed. If the IMA concluded that IUDs caused abortions then no one would be able to fit them as part of a comprehensive family planning service.

I went to Ennis for the day. There were about a hundred doctors present. Many had not even seen an IUD, let alone fitted one. In a brief contribution to the debate I urged that a committee be set up to consider the matter in greater detail and submit a report on how IUDs work. This suggestion was accepted. The Committee members were Brendan Murphy, consultant at the National Maternity Hospital, Ray Hawkins, a GP and member of the IMA Publications Committee, John Bonnar, Professor of Obstetrics and Gynaecology at TCD, Eamon O'Dwyer, Professor of Obstetrics and Gynaecology at UCG, George Henry, and myself. The first of six meetings took place in July. By May 1980, following detailed discussions and reference to thirty-one international publications, we had reached our conclusions and the Committee's report was published in the journal of the IMA in July. While we were unable to give an unequivocal answer, it was agreed that the principal mode of action of the IUD was the production of local changes in the womb lining which prevented a fertilized egg from lodging there. We did not decide whether or not it was abortifacient. I was happy enough with this until I noticed that Committee member Eamon O'Dwyer had been allowed editorial space in the same issue to give an exaggerated account of possible complications arising from the use of an IUD; and to undermine the report by asserting that 'while the Committee has not stated that the intra-uterine device is abortifacient, it has to be conceded that whatever prevents the implantation of a fertilized ovum is, in effect, abortifacient'. O'Dwyer's public 'turnabout' without notifying the other members of the Committee was alarming.

More disastrous repercussions might have followed on from this incident. In September a letter from the Knights of St Columbanus, a private, influential Roman Catholic male organization, was read to a meeting of the Institute of Obstetricians and Gynaecologists. The letter requested that the Institute endorse 'the findings of the IMA committee that IUDs were abortifacient' and should therefore be banned. The basic premise of the Knights' letter was erroneous. After a discussion, members of the Institute decided that, since scientific evidence did not prove that IUDs were abortifacient, they should refuse the Knights' request. Whatever doctors, clerics and politicians thought about the IUD, women continued to come to the clinics asking to be

Eamon O'Dwyer, Professor of Obstetrics and Gynaecology at University College Galway, at an international seminar on natural family planning, 8 October 1979

John Bonnar, Professor of Obstetrics and Gynaecology at Trinity College Dublin, at an anti-abortion conference, 26 September 1980

fitted with the device, and doctors continued to come to us for instruction. Fifteen hundred IUDs were fitted by staff at the clinics that year.

Three years later the IMA dropped another bombshell. As the abortion referendum started to generate heat in 1983 John Bonnar joined Eamon O'Dwyer, making it clear that they both believed the IUD to be abortifacient and wished to dissociate themselves from the report of 1980. As a result of their objections the IMA rescinded the report, publishing the decision in its journal on 23 September. Once again there had been no discussion with the co-authors – hardly correct professional behaviour.

FOUR

1981 — 1992

In view of the acrimony and confusion that has clouded the issue of abortion in this country in the past decade, clarification of some terminology and facts may be of interest. Abortion is the detachment of an embryo or foetus before the twenty-sixth week of pregnancy. The term *embryo* relates to the first eight weeks and *foetus* to later development. A further differentiation is made between *abortion*, which occurs within the first twelve weeks of pregnancy before the development of the placenta (or afterbirth), and a *miscarriage*, which happens after a placenta has formed. The varieties of abortion are classified as follows: *threatened*, in which there is slight bleeding and discomfort; *incomplete*, when bleeding becomes heavy and pain more severe; *complete*, indicating expulsion of the pregnancy, with cessation of bleeding and pain; *septic*, when fever accompanies any of the above; and *induced*, which is occupying the minds of many at present: 12 per cent of all pregnancies can be expected to end in abortion or miscariage.

Induced abortion has been illegal in Ireland since 1861. Clause 58 of the Offences Against the Persons Act laid down a maximum penalty of life imprisonment for any woman who sought to terminate her pregnancy or any person who terminated a pregnancy. Women who wanted an abortion and who had the money travelled to England or the Continent to avail of medical services within those countries. Although a small group, 'A Woman's Right to Choose', had attempted to gain support for legalized abortion, and the larger Society for the Protection of Unborn

Children (SPUC), which had been in operation since 1980, had gone public with its vehement anti-abortion stance, it had never been a national issue. In fact, until the early eighties, no one had shown much interest in the matter.

Like every nation, Ireland has its share of self-appointed moral guardians. Fearing that abortion might be imposed on Ireland by European law, a small but influential conservative pressure group approached the leaders of the two major political parties several weeks before the general election of June 1981. The group claimed that an amendment to the Constitution was required to rule out any possibility that abortion might become available to Irish women within the state, and sought assurances that there would be a referendum on the matter. To a large extent the people putting abortion onto the political agenda were those opposed to the use of contraception and to divorce.

Exercising what Mary Robinson was to refer to in an article in the *Irish Independent* as 'a kind of political self-preservation', the then Taoiseach, Charles Haughey, and the Leader of the Opposition, Garret FitzGerald, accepted the proposal that an amendment to the Constitution should be sought. With a general election looming, this unequivocal acceptance of the demands of a small, private and conservative grouping without any discussion in the Dáil was politically expedient. Both men were fearful that if they were seen to be wavering on the issue they would be labelled as supporters of abortion. Politically this would have been disastrous.

Three general elections took place between June 1981 and November 1982. Ireland was politically unbalanced. With a concentration of internal and external difficulties on its hands no government wanted to cope with the additional pressure the abortion issue would inevitably produce. On 4 November 1982 with the Dáil about to be dissolved, the Fianna Fáil government announced its chosen wording for a referendum to be voted on by the people of Ireland. It read:

'The State acknowledges the right to life of the unborn and, with due regard to the equal right to life of the mother, guarantees in its laws to respect, and, as far as practicable, by its laws to defend and vindicate that right.'

This wording was to cause legal, medical, moral, spiritual and political problems for many people over the course of the referendum campaigns. This wording was to provide the Eighth Amendment to the Irish Constitution. Ultimately, this wording would be used in 1992 to stop a fourteen-year-old girl, pregnant as a result of alleged rape, from leaving the country to avail of abortion services in England as she and her family had decided.

Members of the Pro-Life Amendment Campaign, launched in April 1981, were happy with Fianna Fáil's proposal. Believing that it would fulfil their aims and rule out the introduction of abortion to Ireland, PLAC's medical and legal supporters found nothing to criticize. For myself and the many others who found themselves in the opposition camp the problems seemed insurmountable.

Unhappy with the word 'unborn', recourse to Roget's *Thesaurus* left me even more confused. 'Unborn' is included as an adjective cognate with 'uncreated', 'unconceived', and 'in the womb of time'. Technically the term 'unborn' could be used in relation to future pregnancies, as yet unconceived, in addition to actual pregnancies. If the Amendment were to be interpreted in this way – and who was to say it was not? – it could affect the legality of the use of contraceptives. As a physician who whole-heartedly endorsed the use of contraception, I was worried. 'With due regard', 'as far as practicable', 'the equal right to life of the mother': the wording was a quagmire of possible interpretations. As an obstetrician, a husband and a father I was fearful that women's lives could be put in danger if they were forced to continue with a life-threatening pregnancy. Were the lives of Irish women to be valued on the same level as the unborn baby? There was also the possibility that certain approved treatments of pregnant women, for example a Caesarean section or the induction of labour, could be considered in breach of the law if the baby died. This presented medical staff with the risk of vigilantism in hospital practice. Pro-Life supporters could be on the look-out for possible breaches of the Constitution. Such fears were real. Nursing and medical staff had reported colleagues in the past for performing sterilizations. It was worrying that in the 1980s medical staff should be looking over their shoulders for objections before assessing correct treatment for their patients.

A Fine Gael/Labour Coalition government held office during the ten-month run-up to the referendum. The proposed wording continued to be contentious. In February 1983 Peter Sutherland, the Attorney General, called it 'imprecise and potentially dangerous'. In March the Coalition issued an alternative wording. Within a week the Catholic Hierarchy had pronounced the new wording to be unacceptable to the Church. Meanwhile Dr John Armstrong, the Church of Ireland Primate, stated unequivocally that the original version was equally unacceptable to Protestants. Towards the end of April the Dáil voted, first against the Coalition's wording, and then to approve the original version.

The reactionary groups which supported the Amendment were beginning to mobilize. In 1980 the majority of Catholic doctors had joined the Irish Catholic Doctors' Guild (ICDG). Between then and the passage of the Amendment in September 1983 it is estimated that the cost of their campaign exceeded three-quarters of a million pounds.

Members of the ICDG had participated in an anti-abortion conference at Trinity College in September 1980. The conference had been organized by John Bonnar for 'The World Federation of Doctors Who Respect Human Life'. Many who attended would later play a prominent part in the Pro-Life Amendment Campaign and work alongside some other conservative groups which had also opposed the provision of sex education. The largest and best-known of all these groups was the Society for the Protection of Unborn Children (SPUC). Its membership included Dr Mary Lucey, founder and president, Mrs Patsy Buckley, public relations officer, and Ms Majella Mulkeen, chairwoman of Student Pro-Life. With Senator Des Hanafin and Brendan Shortall as fund-raiser and spokesman respectively, SPUC maintained a high media profile during the campaign and promoted its strongly held ideological views with fervour. Members of the PLAC were politically astute individuals. Despite the fact that there were many seasoned campaigners in the ranks, Julia Vaughan, a former nun who had become a gynaecologist, was selected as their chairwoman. Well-known gynaecologists, the late Eamon de Valera and Kevin Feeney, Arthur Barry, and John Bonnar, encouraged Vaughan in her leading role. As Bonnar commented, it was better to use Vaughan to front the organization rather than 'senior academic gynaecologists who looked like a stuffy old bunch'.

Pamphlets, letters to newspapers and public meetings ensured that the Pro-Lifers' appeal for funds was widely heard. Members of the campaign itself, including many of the medical profession, were known to have made donations. Confirming the PLAC's fervent belief that 'life begins at fertilization', and voicing their concern that 'Article 40 of the Constitution seems to protect the life of the citizen but fails to mention the unborn,' Vaughan said in an interview published in *The Irish Medical Times* of May 1981 that the founding patrons of the campaign, 'eleven eminent male obstetricians and gynaecologists, have made personal financial contributions to the considerable costs that are being incurred'. As the fight to amend the Constitution hotted up, members of the PLAC began to conjure up fears of a global conspiracy of laughing abortionists in the public mind. The treasurer of the PLAC's fund-raising committee, Dr Dominic O'Doherty, claimed in an appeal for money that 'the international abortion movement with its limitless funds will be pitted against us'. This was simply untrue, and provided ample evidence that this was not to be a clean fight.

In May 1982 an active Anti-Amendment campaign was launched. At a press conference on 2 June the Anti-Amendment Campaign called on the Taoiseach, now Charles Haughey, to abandon plans for a referendum, reiterating concerns about the inadequacy of the wording and the potential effects of the Amendment on medical practice. A list of almost a hundred sponsors was published. These came from a wide range of backgrounds: artists, academics, members of the clergy, doctors, journalists, lawyers, TDs and Senators of both sexes. Our list contrasted with the PLAC list of 'founding patrons', which included just eleven gynaecologists, and their 'chairman' Julia Vaughan. Reports, however, did suggest that pro-Amendment doctors countrywide outnumbered those opposing it.The Pro-Life Amendment Campaign had a year's start on the Anti-Amendment Campaign, whose main aim was to ensure members of the public understood what they were voting about. Action groups were encouraged. Meetings with politicians at all levels were requested. We resolved to establish a high profile and to use the media to maximum effect.

Soon afterwards George Henry, then Master of the Rotunda, called a meeting of the hospital's consultants to discuss his anxieties about the proposed Amendment. The staff, Protestant, Catholic and Jewish, decided to contact the Institute of Obstetricians and Gynaecologists (IOG). The Institute represented all of Ireland's consultants and we decided that it should be involved in attempts to clarify some of the problems with the wording and to provide authoritative information about its implications for Irish medical practice. Although the Institute's committee met on a regular basis, the matter was not discussed for a year.

As alarm grew within the ranks of the medical profession 'Amendment fever' spread into legal circles. In-depth legal debate culminated in a statement issued in the week before polling and signed by 600 lawyers. This was more than twice the number of lawyers the Pro-Life campaign said were in favour of the Amendment. 'Flabby, imprecise and dangerous' was how the signatories described the Amendment's wording. It is significant to note that a number of lawyers supporting the principle underlying the Amendment were prepared to vote against it on the grounds that it would create a minefield of legal definition. Challenging the doctors who supported the Amendment, Professor Frank Clarke BL said that he feared the insistence of pro-Amendment doctors that there would be no change in medical practice was based upon a fundamental misunderstanding of how the legal profession works. The PLAC case was that there would be no change because there would be no change in statute law. Clarke pointed out that a constitutional case could be taken irrespective of statute law, and that then it would be up to the courts to interpret the wording they had before them. Doctors would have to abide by legal decisions. The way was also being left open for third-party injunctions to oblige the continuation of a pregnancy even though the woman's life was endangered.

Buswell's Hotel on 25 January 1983 was the venue for another doctors' press conference. Dermot Hourihane, Dean of the Medical School at Trinity College, who chaired the meeting, was joined by Mary Henry, a medical consultant at the Rotunda and member of the IMA's Ethics Committee, Michael Flynn, a family doctor, Ronald Draper, a consultant psychiatrist, Mervyn Taylor, a consultant paediatrician, and myself. Journalists Mary Holland, Jill Nesbitt, Ann O'Donnell from the Rape Crisis Centre and Ann Marie Hourihane were also present. We reiterated criticisms of the Amendment and expressed concern at the creation of a climate of intimidation as allegations like 'baby-murderer' were starting to be used by certain members in the other camp. The statement was counter-signed by over a hundred supporters from all walks of life and a

THE ANTI-AMENDMENT CAMPAIGN

P. O. BOX 1285 DUBLIN 7 PH: 308636

SPONSORS
Mavis Arnold
John Arden
Brian Anderson
Robert Ballagh
Rev. Prof. Jim Barklay
Leland Bardwell
Des Bonass
Prof. Kevin Boyle UCG
Seamus Breathnach
Prof. Ivor Browne
Dr. Noel Browne
Maureen Cairnduff
Pat Carroll
Una Claffey
Paul Clarke
Dr. Conor Cruise O'Brien
Mary Cullen – Lecturer in History, Maynooth
Margarette D'Arcy
Prof. Seamus Deane
Aileen Dillane
Dr. Maire de Paor
Cllr. Jane Dillon-Byrne
Dr. Dolores Dooley-Clarke – Lecturer in Medical Ethics, U.C.C.
Eamonn Dunphy
Philip Flynn
Eric Fleming
Rev. Ernest Gallagher – President, Methodist Church
Rev Dr. Eric Gallagher – Methodist Church
Eddie Glackin
Des Geraghty
Very Rev. Victor Griffin – Dean St. Patrick's Cathedral
Noreen Greene
Judy Hayes
Dr. Mary Heney
Dr. George Henry – Master Rotunda Hospital
Janet Hughes
Michael D. Higgins, T.D.
Eddie Higgins
Brid Horan
Dermot Hourihane – Prof. of Pathology and Dean of the Faculty of Medicine – T.C.D.
Neil Jordan
Jennifer Johnson
Prof. Patrick Keating – T.C.D.
Prof. Norman Gibson – N.U.U.
Mike Kelly
Jim Kemmy T.D.
Dr. Paddy Leahy
Dr. Jim Loughran
Prof. Paddy Lynch
Bernadette MacAliskey
Fiona MacAnna
Sean McCarthy
Marie MacEntee
Catherine McGuiness
Rev. Terence McCaughey
Derek Mahon
Patrick Mason
John MacMenamin
Mat Merrigan
Christy Moore
John Mulcahy
Rosemary Mulcahy
Finbar Murphy
David Norris
Eilean Ni Chuilleanain
Mary O'Donnell
Risteard O Glaisne
Fiona Poole
Thomas Pakenham
Hilary Pratt
Peter Prendergast
Pat Rabbitte
Sen. Mary Robinson
Sen. Shane Ross
Dr. Andrew Rynne
Patrick Scott
Ronan Sheehan
Andree Sheehy Skeffington
Camille Souter
Niall Stokes
Rev. Peter Tarleton
Sen. Trevor West
Brigid Wilkinson
Prof. John Whyte – Q.U.B.
Dr. Maura Woods
Rev. Stanley Worrall
Brenda Weir
Prof. Donald Weir

ORGANISATIONS
Bolton St. Students Union
Cherish
Communist Party of Ireland
Dublin Well Woman Centre
Galway Labour Womens Group
Irish Pregnancy Counselling Centre
Irish Republican Socialist Party
Rape Crisis Centre
Trade Union Womens' Forum
Union of Students in Ireland
People's Democracy
Democratic Socialist Party
Right to Choose Group
Right to Choose Campaign
Irish Council for Civil Liberties

21st. January, 1983.

P R E S S   R E L E A S E

DOCTORS AGAINST THE AMENDMENT will be launched on Tuesday, 25th. January 1983 at 5.00 p.m. in Buswell's Hotel, Molesworth Street (Oriel Room)

-o-

A list of over 100 doctors who have signed a statement of opposition to the proposed Constitutional amendment will be released and the Press Conference will be addressed by, among other doctors:

Professor Dermot Hourihane,
Dean of the School of Medicine,
Trinity College Dublin

Dr. Mary Henry, Consultant Physician

Dr. Michael Solomons, M.D. F.R.C.O.G.,
F.R.C.P.I.

---oOo---

The Anti-Amendment Campaign press release launching 'Doctors Against the Amendment' in Buswell's Hotel, Dublin, 25 January 1983

corresponding number of doctors. It indicated no denominational divide.

During the conference a request came through from Radio Eireann for a three-minute interview on the 6.30 news bulletin. With only twenty minutes before transmission there was little opportunity to discuss who should go and I was duly dispatched. Shane Kenny went easy on me and the interview was relaxed enough until the end, when he asked: 'Do you think the Amendment is sectarian?' I paused, but the answer was obvious. Dermot Hourihane wrote the next day: 'Many thanks for participating yesterday. I hope we may have started something but I feel better already whatever happens.'

I had been hesitant about saying the Amendment was sectarian on national radio but I should not have been. The Amendment put pressure on people to display loyalty to their own Church at the cost of withholding their customary understanding of others. Victor Griffin, Dean of St Patrick's Cathedral, Dublin, made a statement in February 1983. Referring to the proposed Amendment he said: 'The wording is ambiguous. Many other national problems are being ignored and deserve priority. Abortion should be allowed as a last resort in certain unfortunate exceptional cases. Everyone has a right to his or her own opinion, and enshrining one particular denominational opinion in the Constitution is sectarian. It is one more example of our sex-obsessed society. Do we want a Roman Catholic confessional state or a pluralist traditional society?'

'Politically hypocritical, socially divisive, morally questionable and economically irresponsible', was how the Chief Rabbi, Dr David Rosen, referred to the Amendment in September 1983. Rosen said that members of the Jewish community could not support the Amendment in good faith because in Jewish teaching the sanctity of the life of the mother was above that of the embryo. He added in an interview in the *Dublin Jewish News* that, although Jewish law prohibits wanton destruction and does not permit abortion on demand, it does allow abortion if 'qualified medical opinion considers a pregnancy to be a serious threat to the physical and mental health of the mother'.

When does life begin? This is the question at the heart of any consideration of the medical practice of abortion. There is, of course, no definitive answer. Different individuals, cultures and denominations hold different views. This makes the imposition of a single view of abortion on an entire people seem ludicrous. It is worth noting that Catholic doctrine concerning ensoulment (the beginning of life) and abortion changed at least six times between the third century and 1869, when Pope Pius IX reaffirmed the belief that life begins at conception, and decreed against the practice of abortion. Pius's rigorous views were enshrined in the 1918 Code of Canon Law and are used by the Church today. However, further change remains a possibility.

The Church of Ireland also believes that human life begins at conception, while making a distinction between biological life and being a person. Abortion is rejected, 'save at the dictate of strict and undeniable medical necessity'.

Rabbinic opinions on when life begins do not provide a definitive answer. David Rosen told me in March 1983 that some Jewish scholars believe life begins when the baby's movements can be felt, while others believe it starts at the time of birth. The term 'unborn' has no place in Rabbinic doctrine.

Islam teaches that the soul is 'inspired' no earlier than 40 days and no later than 120 days after conception. Abortion is permitted for gross foetal abnormalities and maternal indications up to 120 days but after this only if the mother's life is seriously threatened. There are some 5000 Muslims living in Ireland.

As both campaigns gathered momentum early in 1983 RTE invited both groups to engage in a televised discussion of the issues on the 'Today Tonight' programme, although it was still a possibility that the Attorney General and the

Senator Mary Robinson addressing a rally against the Amendment, in the Mansion House, Dublin, 2 February 1983

Director of Public Prosecutions might defer the referendum. Our team was made up of Mary Henry, Kevin Boyle, Professor of Law at UCG, and myself. We were briefed on the art of presentation by two supportive telecommunications advisers. At Montrose in the make-up room we met the PLAC team of Julia Vaughan, Eamon O'Dwyer and William Binchy, a prominent barrister and their legal adviser. The presenter John Bowman kept us well in check.

Over a hundred doctors attended a major Anti-Amendment meeting at the Shelbourne Hotel on 31 May. The late Fergus Meehan and Michael Mylotte were on the platform. Both men were Catholics and gynaecologists. They were colleagues of O'Dwyer at the Regional Hospital in Galway. It was another example of how the country and the medical profession were being split in two by the debate. Whole families would find themselves divided over the issue by the time the campaigning had run its course.

The national newspapers were awash with letters for and against the Amendment. Both sides used the correspondence columns as a way of attracting public attention. It was how these letters were used that became problematic. Six of the founding patrons of PLAC, John Bonnar, the late Eamon de Valera and Kevin Feeney, David Jenkins, Kieran O'Driscoll and Eamon O'Dwyer, wrote to the newspapers publicizing their support for the referendum and the Amendment. They clearly identified themselves as professors in university medical schools in Dublin, Cork and Galway, and affirmed their 'firm conviction that the Amendment will not interfere with existing medical practice in the treatment of pregnant patients'. 'The professors' letter', as it became known, was to form the corner-stone of subsequent PLAC propaganda.

Looking at our correspondence in mid-June, many doctors were surprised to find a letter from Stanley Hewitt, the chairman of the Institute of Obstetricians and Gynaecologists. Hewitt, a founding patron of the Pro-Life

Amendment Campaign, wrote: 'I wish to state categorically that the skilled treatment available to every pregnant woman in Ireland will not be altered in any way whatsoever, whether there is an Amendment or not. I should also like to reassure all my colleagues that there is not the slightest added risk of any legal proceedings being taken against any of them should the present wording be written into the Constitution.' The national press leapt on the statement, reporting it in full. In turn I wrote to him 'envying his crystal ball', as no one could possibly foresee with certainty how the practice of medicine might change if the Amendment were introduced.

On 19 June at a meeting of the Institute's council, of which I was not a member, Hewitt stated that the document had been intended only 'for discussion' and should have been sent only to council members. He said that he deeply regretted what had happened, particularly the disclosure of the contents of the letter to the national press. After a lively discussion the council prepared a statement which made it clear that Hewitt's letter merely indicated his personal and private views on the matter and did not represent the Institute. It was evident, however, that the Institute as a professional medical body should try to establish its attitude towards the referendum. Members of the council took a decision to call an extraordinary general meeting. There was to be a single item on the agenda: 'That the Institute should discuss the proposed wording of the Amendment and its possible consequences for the practice of Obstetrics and Gynaecology.'

All members were sent a notice informing them about the meeting and stating that it had been scheduled to take place on 22 July 1983. Two weeks later we received another letter indicating that proxy voting would be allowed. It contained a form which those who were unable to attend were meant to fill in and return. The form required that people indicate if in their view 'the wording of the proposed Constitutional amendment will / will not in my opinion affect the future practice of Obstetrics in Ireland'.

The time had come to depend on more than gut feeling and personal experience. I wrote to the President of the Royal College of Obstetricians and Gynaecologists in London asking for the authoritative views of the College on when life begins. In reply he stated that there was no agreed scientific opinion on the matter. I had also written to the Medical Protection Society asking the same question through their representatives in Dublin, Arthur Cox and Company. The Society advises doctors on any allegations of malpractice involving litigation and offers insurance cover. I received the same reply.

Unwilling to leave such an important issue to chance, I contacted Adrian Hardiman, a senior barrister, and arranged to send him copies of my recent correspondence with the Institute, together with the by-laws of the Royal College of Physicians in Ireland (RCPI), the Institute's parent body. Hardiman was to give his views on the validity of the proposed proxy vote. Refusing to accept a fee, Hardiman gave me his opinion as counsel on 18 July. It read: 'A proxy vote is not permissible at a meeting of the Institute' and that, in any case, 'the proposed form of postal voting did not constitute a proxy'.

An hour before the EGM on 22 July, consultants from the Rotunda met at the hospital to discuss strategy. George Henry and I were delegated to lead the argument against the referendum and the rest were to back us up when we ran out of steam. Arriving at the meeting, which took place in the historic hall of the College, we found that only about thirty of the Institute's ninety members had turned up. The low attendance was in all probability a direct result of the Institute's declared intention to allow proxy voting. The air was thick with tension. The battle-lines had been drawn. Gynaecologists who supported the Amendment sat on one side of the hall, its opponents sat on the other.

Hewitt, the chairman, was a highly respected consultant and a friend, but despite the fact that he was usually an efficient chairman, he had not considered that the by-laws, the rules and procedures, of the RCPI might prove relevant to the proceedings. No one, apart from myself, had brought a copy and not all of those present were Fellows of the College. Hewitt opened the meeting and commented that many proxy votes had been received and would be considered at the appropriate time. Quoting the legal opinion I had received from Adrian Hardiman, I objected to the acceptance of the proxy votes. When the fact that proxy voting was invalid had sunk in the meeting took off. Before the evening was over, the grand hall of the College was to become a bear-pit as speakers continually interrupted and heckled each other.

Arguments for and against the Amendment were repeated and requoted from the many pamphlets and letters which had appeared over the preceding months. 'The professors' letter' was singled out for particular criticism. We in the Anti-Amendment corner said that the six Institute members had acted unilaterally in publishing such a letter, which merely represented the personal views of the six, all of whom were present. The main purpose of the meeting was to agree on the approach to the Amendment that we should adopt as a professional body. Therefore we claimed that the Institute should take the opportunity to formulate and issue a statement. PLAC supporters objected strongly, fearful that any statement we issued would jeopardize the persuasive effect that the 'professors' letter' was undoubtedly continuing to have. A vote was taken. The members voted to instruct the chairman to issue a statement; however, the result was ruled out as it had not been passed by a two-thirds majority. When someone pointed out that there was no such rule in the College by-laws, Hewitt had no option but to let the vote stand.

PLAC members, their feathers ruffled, then played what appeared to be their trump card. The evening's meeting was itself 'out of order' as thirty days' notice of the motion had not been given since it had been modified on 28 June. The

An Anti-Abortion march in Dublin, 12 May 1979

chairman agreed and we stood by as several PLAC supporters left the meeting in triumph. Unknown to many we had one last trick up our sleeves. Another look at the by-laws produced an overtrump: the thirty-day rule applied only to annual general meetings. Once we had obtained permission to speak again and quoted the relevant reference, the meeting erupted. Such a mixture of anger, abuse and cheers can rarely have been heard in the college's long history. Patients would have been appalled to hear how their generally well-mannered consultants could behave. Hewitt rightly decided upon a break to allow things to cool off.

Realizing that Stanley Hewitt might be fed up with the constant interruptions, and wishing to show him that my part in the proceedings was in no way directed at him personally, I approached the committee table for a chat. Others joined us. One angrily demanded to see my copy of the college by-laws. Not happy with this aggressive interruption I refused and was astonished to find that I risked receiving a punch on the jaw. Removal of my glasses in preparation for an active defence was enough to abort the threat and I am pleased to say that the confrontation was in no way as serious as when I won my school's flea-weight boxing championship in 1929.

Finally calm returned and we agreed on the form of the statement that was to be issued: 'The meeting could not reach a consensus of opinion with regard to the implication for medical practice should the proposed Amendment to the Constitution be carried.'

A week later in an article, 'The Amendment and Medical Practice' in the *Irish Independent*, Bruce Arnold noted the lack of agreement amongst gynaecologists of the implications for Irish women of acceptance of the Amendment. Some, as has already been stated, were confident that medical practice would not be affected and that the rights of women would not be pushed into second place behind those of the foetus. Others were not so sure.

Even before the Anti-Amendment campaign there must have been doctors, and I was one, who considered the termination of pregnancy as advisable in certain exceptional cases. Some were clear-cut: cancer of the womb or breast, severe heart disease, obstetrical histories indicating a dangerously high risk, acute psychological disorders, and other conditions such as renal failure and hypertension that had not responded to treatment and that an experienced physician considered would affect the life-expectancy of the mother. In addition, rape and incest were sufficient violations in themselves not to be compounded by an on-going pregnancy.

Other cases were more complex. Listening to women's stories in my role as a physician I came to realize that no issue connected with abortion is simple or straightforward, black or white. One mother brought her eighteen-year-old pregnant daughter to me saying the girl's father would disown her if he found out. Another mother came to me distraught. Her mentally handicapped daughter was pregnant and the mother believed that a continuing pregnancy would be devastating. Young women would come to me in tears. Thinking that they were in a stable relationship they had become pregnant and the man in their life had deserted them. Other women came saying they would lose their jobs if they had a child. Parents of families who were already under severe economic stress said that they just could not face having another child to fend for.

Abortion should never be considered an alternative to responsible sexual activity and the use of contraception, or 'on demand'. Doctors whose beliefs permit consideration of requests for abortion do not look on the matter lightly. A doctor will always insist on detailed discussion before agreeing to refer a patient for a termination. As a doctor practising in a state where there were no facilities for abortion, I made it my business to assess such facilities in a state that did allow the procedure. I visited a clinic run by the British Pregnancy Advisory Service, a non-profit-making body, in England. It was possible to make appointments by telephone for the few cases I referred before 1983. Each patient needed to bring a medical report in accordance with the regulations of the UK Abortion Act of 1967. She would be interviewed by qualified counsellors before the operation. This counselling was obligatory. The patient would return to me for a check-up and advice concerning the future.

Those who travel outside the state without any counselling deserve compassion and understanding, even from those opposed to abortion. They are desperate, often distraught, women, having to concoct plausible excuses for being away from home or jobs. Afraid of the unknown, they face a lonely journey. They have to meet their travel and accommodation costs, and often the cost of the operation itself. They travel, hoping that they will not be found out, while the men who are responsible often ignore their plight. According to figures taken from the UK Registrar General's 1991 report, 3721 women from the Republic and 1816 women from the North travelled to England in 1989 to obtain an abortion. These statistics are considered an underestimate because of the need for anonymity. Ireland continues to export its problems, while the solution to so many of them lies in her own backyard. When housing and unemployment improve, when adequate parent/child and male/female relationships exist, when there is an adequate health and education service which encourages awareness of sex and sexuality, and when a comprehensive and accessible contraceptive service is available in rural as well as urban areas, these terrible statistics will start to drop.

August 1983 was a hectic month. I was informed that Fianna Fáil's final wording of the Amendment had been described by Haughey himself as 'the best that could be devised to obtain TDs' approval'. As the days progressed, the debate about the Amendment and the substantive issue of abortion became more vicious. The country was being torn in two.

With three weeks to go, at an Anti-Amendment conference in Buswell's Hotel we again stated our view that the Amendment could kill women. Adrian Hardiman appealed to Catholic priests not to create division and bitterness within the active membership of the Church by turning churches into political platforms. It was probably too little, too late. There had already been many examples of priests urging their congregations to support the Amendment, saying it had God's blessing. The Amendment also had papal support: 'If the Pope were an Irishman on Wednesday, he would be voting "yes",' Father Coleman Carrigy, curate at the church of the Holy Trinity in Ballinalee, Co. Longford, told his parishioners.

PLAC held their conference the next day. A strong abortion lobby was at work behind the façade of the Anti-Amendment campaign, claimed Dr Kevin McNamara, the Bishop of Kerry, in a statement to a PLAC meeting at a convent in County Clare on 16 August. Tomás MacGiolla, then President of the Workers' Party, and Labour Party TD Justin Keating were among those who condemned it as a ridiculous thing to say, 'lacking the reason and logic expected of a former Professor of Theology at Maynooth'.

Politicians were under attack. Responsibility for the rancour resulting from the Amendment campaign was laid firmly at their door. Eileen Desmond TD attacked her own party for the dreadful way in which they had handled the whole affair. Monica Barnes TD described the wording as 'Deliberately vague, ambiguous, and downright dangerous – even deadly.'

The PLAC professors moved again, sending a letter to nursing staff in hospitals across the country. The letter read, 'We the undersigned matron and nurses of — fully support the Pro-Life Amendment to the Constitution, to protect unborn life and prevent abortion. We also affirm our firm conviction that the Amendment will not interfere with existing medical practice in the treatment of pregnant patients.' This tactic of asking nurses to agree on an aspect of

Voting at a polling station in Clane, Co. Kildare, on referendum day, 7 September 1983

medical practice for which they had no direct responsibility was illogical.

Gynaecologists in the Anti-Amendment camp were anxious to counter the claims of PLAC's supporters in the medical profession. Conor Carr from Ballinasloe, Anton Dempsey, George Henry and myself met in Nenagh to prepare a statement for release to the media. The statement, signed by Carr, Ian Dalrymple, Dempsey, Vincent Fenton, Henry, Stephen Long, Fergus Meehan, Michael Mylotte, Alistair McFarlane, Tim O'Connor, Edgar Ritchie and myself, was included in the RTE evening news bulletins on 18 August 1983 and reported in the newspapers the following day.

The impression coming from some pulpits was that good Catholics should vote 'yes' to the Amendment, putting aside any regard for the feelings, beliefs or opinions of others. Prominent members of the clergy like Dr Conway, Bishop of Elfin, and Dr Hegarty, Bishop of Raphoe, denied this. The PLAC campaign was neither divisive nor sectarian, and definitely not a political issue, they told pilgrims at Knock in late August. Ultimately Archbishop Dermot Ryan was to intervene directly in the political debate over the referendum, urging people to support the Amendment in a letter read out at all Masses in Dublin on 4 September.

The newspapers were naturally filled with details of the campaigns and political and religious polemic. My own contribution had appeared in the *Irish Independent* on 2 September. The wording, I argued, made it impossible for people to express two opinions with one vote. There was no way that those who wished to could register agreement with a ban on legal abortion and yet disagree with the notion that the 'unborn' should enjoy equal rights with the mother. Truth had become a casualty of the campaign. The integrity of some professional colleagues and the trust that the public were supposed to have in doctors' judgments had been severely damaged. If the Amendment were passed it would prove that a small group of people, aggressive, vocal, well organized and well funded, could impose their views on the state. What issue would they turn to next?

'What will we find to talk about when the referendum is over?' asked Dick Walsh in *The Irish Times*. 'Nothing,' he concluded. 'By the time it's over most of us won't be talking to each other.'

Despite all the talk, the hellfire and damnation, the Irish electorate did not turn out to vote in large numbers. Compared with the usual 70–75 per cent poll for general elections, the 54 per cent on 7 September looked rather paltry. We in the Anti-Amendment campaign had known that there was no way we could win, and we were not dissatisfied to note that the PLAC had inspired only a 2:1 majority in favour of the Amendment.

PLAC supporters interpreted the vote as vindication of their moral and spiritual beliefs. The Church and the Pro-Life campaigners called for the creation of 'a caring society in which abortion would not be seen as the answer to any human problem'. There is little to disagree with in this statement. In the perfect world there would be no need for abortion. But this is not a perfect world and we are far from the creation of that 'caring society'.

Only four years before the 1983 referendum, the Dublin Rape Crisis Centre opened its doors for the first time. Sexual crimes are not a modern problem. What is new is the increasing ability to report and discuss them, and the development of public concern. The invaluable support given to victims by Olive Braiden and her staff at the Centre has brought progressively increasing numbers seeking help. First visits to the DRCC in 1991, relating to adult rape, sexual assault and child sexual abuse, totalled 1660. Interviews with victims indicate that sexual abuse is often inflicted by family and family friends. Many are coerced into silence. Some have bottled-up memories of abuse for years through a misplaced sense of shame and guilt. Men who commit rape and women victims have often suffered

A Defend the Clinics campaign on O'Connell Bridge, Dublin, 10 October 1987

sexual abuse themselves in childhood. It is a tragic cycle, and one at the very centre of the debate.

During the course of the Anti-Amendment campaign we had warned people that there was a possibility that it might be used to infringe personal liberty. We had constantly insisted that the wording was ill-conceived and dangerous. No one who opposed the Amendment, however, actually wanted to be proved right.

In February of 1992 the 'nightmare scenario' came to pass. What was worse, it happened to a fourteen-year-old girl who had been allegedly sexually abused and made pregnant as a result of rape. The Attorney General, Mr Harry Whelehan, applied to the courts for an injunction to restrain the young girl from travelling to England, or any other country, to obtain an abortion. The injunction, granted by the High Court, prohibited the girl from leaving the country for nine months. Her parents, who fully supported their daughter in her wish to have the pregnancy terminated, were forbidden by the order from helping her to procure an abortion.

The Supreme Court reversed the High Court ruling. Irish women do have the right to terminate a pregnancy which represents a 'real and substantial threat' to the mother's life, ruled the judges. In this case the Court said that the girl had repeatedly threatened to kill herself, and so the physical life of the mother was indeed at risk.

PLAC had taken great pains to point out that the referendum would change nothing. Nevertheless, it has been used as a campaigning tool to shut down women's counselling services, to censor women's magazines, to get women's health books removed from public libraries, and to ensure that newspapers containing abortion information are seized at airports and destroyed.

We drift through uncharted waters. As a nation we find ourselves looking to our legislators and lawyers for a solution. The 'flabby, imprecise and dangerous' wording of the Eighth Amendment has proven to be precisely that.

Cartoon from The Irish Times *17 February 1992*
(courtesy *Martyn Turner)*

CONCLUSION

> 'It is almost a definition of a gentleman to say he is one who never inflicts pain.' (John Henry Newman, first rector of the Catholic University of Ireland, 1852)

During my medical career I was made aware of the pain caused by the repressive and intrusive attitude of the Church as it impinged upon the individual's private life. Together with others similarly concerned, we succeeded in providing some help. In spite of all threats to the contrary, allegiance to the Church has remained constant. On 31 May 1992 Cardinal Cahal Daly's homily at Knock concluded: 'The statistics of religious practice have remained remarkably consistent over the last two decades of rapid and unprecedented social and economic change in Ireland.' The results of a 1991 Gallup Poll investigating aspects of religious practices in ten European countries confirmed this, showing Malta topping the list with Ireland second and third in all but one of the questions included in the survey.

There are significant differences between the 1983 referendum and the debate facing us now. Nine years ago a referendum to amend the Constitution was demanded by a small group of people who firmly believed that the law of the land on abortion was inadequate to prevent a challenge by an appeal to European courts: 35.79 per cent of the electorate voted for the Amendment, 17.6 per cent against it, and 46.61 per cent didn't vote at all. Today there are two new issues: one relates to problems arising from an actual case, the other to the Supreme Court ruling that resulted.

The Pro-Life campaigners call the Supreme Court's decision 'astonishing and bizarre', adding it 'clearly flew in the face of the obvious intent of the voters in 1983'. To refer in this way to the judgment of the highest court in the land is both arrogant and irresponsible. To claim to know what the electorate of 1983 intended when half of them expressed no opinion is absurd.

The 'X' case, as it is known, aside from individual and family tragedy, raises complex questions for us all. Sexual abuse of adults, and particularly of children, is anathema to the ordinary citizen, yet the increasing number of cases reported cannot be ignored. Social workers, counsellors and therapists do their best, but they are too few to cope with the scale of the problem.

The Irish National Teachers' Organization and the Eastern Health Board are taking steps to identify those children at risk or already suffering. At a conference in April 1992 a teacher stated, 'at a conservative estimate, 3–4 per cent of our children would suffer from severe or prolonged sexual abuse before they reached eighteen years of age'. In a population of over one million children under sixteen, there must be many hundred adults in our midst responsible for these crimes. The 'X' case involved alleged rape of a minor and an abortion, both subjects of additional importance in view of impending legislation or a referendum. Prior to the Maastricht Treaty vote in June, the Irish Catholic Bishops Conference expressed its views on its implications, in a statement concentrating on the abortion issue. Paragraph 8, 'Pregnancy from incest or rape', reads:

When the pregnancy is the result of incest or rape the experience of the girl or the woman is truly horrific. She may react with resentment, anger or rejection of the pregnancy, which she can feel to be a continuation of the violation of her body. Nevertheless, however abhorrent or degrading the circumstances of the conception, a new human life has come into existence. It is an innocent human life, a life given by God and called to live with God forever, a life which has a right to be welcomed into the human community. To end this life is a further violation of the woman's body and may only increase her distress.

Such a moral judgment has little justification. A rape cannot be God's will. A victim has lost control of her body and has suffered physical violation and psychological damage. It is unlikely that she will be able to make a rational decision about anything for some time. If she discovers she is pregnant, further problems will arise. The measured conclusion of the bishops is remote from the reality of these tragedies. Not only is it remote; the victim has been at the physical mercy of one or more men. What must she feel like if the most powerful group of men in the country avails of its moral force to insist on further use of her body without her consent? While all agree that rape is morally wrong, I cannot recall any strongly worded statement from the Church condemning the offence.

The problem involves more than the woman alone. Without men there would be no abortions. Actions men take may drive women to contemplate terminating a pregnancy, but where is the concomitant condemnation of men? Just as civil law applies to all citizens, moral laws should surely be even-handed, or they lose credibility.

In my religion healing is paramount and the life of the mother always takes precedence over that of the foetus. My upbringing and experience lead me to disagree with much that the Hierarchy say and write, while recognizing and respecting their anxiety and concern. They appear to me as staff officers, while I was an infantryman on the ground: and there is rarely great sympathy between the two.

One Irish result of the Gallup Poll is at odds with others. The question was asked: 'Is the Church giving adequate answers to the moral problems and needs of the individual?' In 1981 52 per cent said 'yes', whereas in 1991 only 41 per cent agreed. Ireland showed the greatest drop of all the countries polled.

The INTO is currently running a 'Stay Safe' campaign in conjunction with the Department of Health. This is an interesting programme, involving teachers and parents, to help children avoid physical and sexual abuse.

There is a parallel to be found between an abused child and an abused society. We all take time to reach maturity. An abused or bullied child will have greater difficulty in achieving this. The problems for a country emerging from the shadow of colonial domination are not solved overnight. Have we at last come to terms with the pain inflicted on past generations? Have we found our identity? Are we now self-reliant enough to take decisions for ourselves?

With improved education and international involvement, people in Ireland have become more confident, efficient and assured, respectful of but not dominated by the past, and more concerned about the future. Such people should be responsible for their actions, and for their bodies.

Abortion is an emotive subject. It requires dispassionate discussion without noisy rallies and mob oratory. Neither women, nor men, lightly take the thought, let alone the step, of abortion. Otherwise the experience is associated with deep and lasting pain. We could do a lot worse than to remember Cardinal Newman, and to try to be 'gentlepersons'.